JAMES KING

OLD MASTERS

Cormorant Books

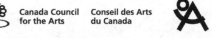

The publisher gratefully acknowledges the support of the Canada Council for the
Arts and the Ontario Arts Council for its publishing program. We acknowledge the
financial support of the Government of Canada through the Canada Book Fund
(CBF) for our publishing activities, and the Government of Ontario through the
Ontario Media Development Corporation, an agency of the Ontario Ministry of
Culture, and the Ontario Book Publishing Tax Credit Program.

LIBRARY AND ARCHIVES CANADA CATALOGUING IN PUBLICATION

King, James, 1942–, author
Old masters / James King.

Issued in print and electronic formats.
ISBN 978-1-77086-422-1 (PBK.). — ISBN 978-1-77086-423-8 (HTML)

I. TITLE.

PS8571.I52837O43   2014C813'.54   C2014-905128-X
C2014-905129-8

Cover design: Angel Guerra/Archetype
Interior text design: Tannice Goddard, Soul Oasis Networking
Printer: Friesens

Printed and bound in Canada.

MIX
Paper from
responsible sources
FSC® C016245

The interior of this book is printed on 100% post-consumer waste recycled paper.

CORMORANT BOOKS INC.
10 ST. MARY STREET, SUITE 615, TORONTO, ONTARIO, M4Y 1P9
www.cormorantbooks.com

For Sheila Malloy

Begin by learning to draw and paint like the old masters. After that, you can do as you like; everyone will respect you.

SALVADOR DALÍ

To my mind the old masters are not art; their value is in their scarcity.

THOMAS EDISON

PART ONE

INCONGRUITIES

CHAPTER ONE

My publisher, Henry Duval, dispatched an email on Friday afternoon requesting the pleasure (his word) of meeting with me at my earliest convenience. Perhaps at ten on Monday morning? he asks.

Though couched as a question, the directive fills me with dread. As a grown-up, supposedly mature middle-aged man, I should be impervious to such assaults. But the email has reduced me to a mound of quivering jelly.

If he had invited me to lunch, I would not be quite so intimidated. Lunch would signal that I am still someone of status, that I remain an accepted member of his depleting stable of writers. A meeting in his chambers, however, spells trouble.

THE WEEKEND IS unbearable. What wrong have I committed? Are my sales figures as bad as all that? Has someone launched an action against me for libel or plagiarism? Has Duval "taken a bath" on my latest book — meaning, has he paid too much for the title?

If Duval is in difficulty, I — who am forever living on the precipice of financial extermination — will be in even greater danger. What grown-up these days lives like I do? A husband and father renting a bedsitter in Cricklewood, employed as a sales clerk at the Waterstone's in Easthampstead, whose wife held him in thrall for five thrilling years before deciding he was unlikely to ever amount to much and running away with a software entrepreneur whose financial prowess compensated for his obesity and his being twenty years her senior.

I met Duval about the time Stella and I parted. "This novel of yours has real potential in today's marketplace," he began, playing Prospero to my Caliban at that first meeting in his office. "Of course it's crude and unfocused, but what with a little hocus pocus I'm sure we can turn it into a tiny masterpiece."

Duval told me, in his endlessly circuitous manner, that he and his associates at Spoonbill Press were old hands at acquiring first novels from young would-be Tolstoys on the cheap and sanitizing them for the genteel, refined tastes of the English book-buying public. "We are fascinated by boldness," he said, "but we remain committed to good manners." He gestured in the direction of the next-door office. "Everything I know about this business I know from Carstairs."

During the five years I have been a Spoonbill hack, the door to Carstairs's office has never been shut. Behind this door a huge Georgian mahogany desk can be seen holding pride of place, and hand-coloured Rowlandson engravings — in which aristocrats and tarts hobnob and celebrate musical evenings at Vauxhall — grace the walls.

I have never encountered the senior partner. "I am very anxious you meet Carstairs," Duval has told me on more than one occasion. "He takes a special interest in your work. He feels that you embody the high standards of the Spoonbill imprint."

My sales, however, are not what Mr. Carstairs might desire. After I received what I was assured were "astonishingly" high advances of £2,000 each for my first two novels, I was reduced to £1,000 for my last. That sad effort received good notices but "flat" sales, as Duval put it.

I am being summoned, I am certain, to be informed that there will be no more novels, and no more advances, no matter how paltry.

AFTER SPENDING THE entire weekend on tenterhooks, preparing myself for a death sentence, I board the crowded Northern Line train down to Charing Cross.

The Charing Cross and Leicester Square area of London has long surrendered itself to earnest American tourists in their fifties, Eurotrash in their twenties, and homegrown teenagers from Metroland, the outer reaches of the Tube. Here, fast food and literary culture have forged a dubious alliance. Cheap take-out restaurants, steakhouses, McDonald's, and dilapidated porn cinemas abound. Plunked down amidst these are the survivors: specialty and used bookshops.

Spoonbill's suite of offices — really a collection of three rooms and a grubby reception area — is two floors over Saunders', the used book dealer. I have often wondered if Carstairs owns Saunders' and immediately consigns his publications to their shelves, but have always been deterred from checking by the dismal faces of the clerks sitting at the front desk, as well as the noxious smells emanating from the miscellany of take-out foods on which they gorge themselves.

The building has no lift, so I trudge up the stairs to the Spoonbill reception area. The grey wall-to-wall carpeting is liberally decorated with coffee spills of various sizes, and strips of Formica wood peel off the receptionist's desk.

Duval is there this morning, dressed as usual in what is still called a Savile Row suit. By my reckoning he has three: black, blue pinstripe, and a hideous chocolate brown. All are single-breasted with side vents, and were probably purchased many years ago in a buy-two-get-three offer. He is not comfortable in any of these outfits because he has become significantly larger since he was measured for them. His jacket is at least two sizes too small, and a large belly protrudes over his belt. Patches of grey hair rise mutinously around the back of his bald head. The cuffs of his shirt are frayed. He is not the picture of prosperity.

Beaming, Duval looks in the direction of his secretary. "Ruth, is Mr. Carstairs in yet?"

She shakes her head.

"I was hoping the old boy would join us today. Have you ever seen his office?" he asks me, in the way of one perfectly conversant with the answer. "Why don't we take a peek?"

Duval pushes me gently towards Carstairs's open door. As soon as I cross the threshold, I can plainly see what I have always suspected: this is a non-working office. There is no computer, not even a laptop, and a fine mist of dust covers everything in sight. The Rowlandson prints are cheap late-nineteenth-century, the colours probably applied by hand in China. After walking to the window, where the once-white curtains are now a deep beige, we turn and are confronted by a hideous imitation of a Thomas Gainsborough.

"Mr. Carstairs's great-grandfather, Ralph," Duval tells me. "He was evidently a simple country parson, yet significant enough for the great Tom to paint him."

Though the style is in the manner of Gainsborough, the great painter would have found some way to enhance his sitter's countenance with a semblance of humanity. In this portrait, however, the eyes that leer at me are exceedingly small and recessed, the wig is in tatters, and the nose is bulbous. This imitation is not even by a follower of Gainsborough. It is by an incompetent who saw a canvas or two by the great painter before setting up shop.

As if reading my mind, Duval assures me, "Mr. Carstairs has all the documentation proving the authenticity of this noble portrait."

Some people will believe anything.

"Well, if Carstairs is not pitching up today, we shall retreat to my office."

I am relieved that the senior partner is, per usual, absent — perhaps due to a serious health issue, if he has inherited his ancestor's genes. I am better off with the devil I know.

"I am exceedingly sorry that we could not offer you lunch today," Duval says. "My schedule is set in stone, and I could not shift anything." He asks if I will "take" a glass of sherry.

I am dumfounded. Duval is taking a long time to do me in. Perhaps there is a bit of guilt lingering in his conscience?

My surprise ends when he begins the familiar litany: Sales are down sharply. The Internet is killing book sales. No one knows what havoc ebooks will bring in their wake. The economy is in the doldrums. No one reads anymore. These commonplaces he relates to me as grand truths.

"We are not in a position at the moment to commission a new narrative from you, although I know how sparkling it would be. That is the reality that confronts us at Spoonbill." He pauses, and crocodile tears begin to form in his eyes.

For a brief moment, I allow myself to feel a modicum of sympathy for this fellow who, twenty years ago, may have become a publisher because he loved books. Then I decide to brush aside sentimental musings. I sit up straight and, like a brave soldier unjustly accused and convicted of treason, wait for the judgment of the court martial.

Duval suddenly changes course. "Guy, am I correct to think you Canadian?"

What does that have to do with anything?

"Yes. Technically. I am a citizen of both the United Kingdom and Canada. I was born in Mississauga, a suburb of Toronto, but my parents returned to the UK when I was three years old. I don't remember anything about the place and have never been back."

"Yes. I remember you telling me so." He rests his head in his hands, then meets my eyes again. "That made us think of you. A fascinating congruence."

"Congruence?"

"Yes. As soon as I mentioned to Mr. Carstairs that you were born in Canada, he was certain you would be the perfect man for the job."

"Job?"

"We had the most splendid proposition made to us last week. You undoubtedly know of Gabriel Brown?"

I confess that I know of no such person.

Duval is dismayed. "Not know about the world-famous dealer in Old Masters? The notice was in all the papers."

"I only read *The Guardian*. Would they have covered it?"

"My dear man, tributes filled even their pages! I have caught you asleep at the wheel — you have had too many late nights toiling at Waterstone's. Gabriel Brown, your fellow countryman, came to London in 1945 towards the end of the Hitler War. After he was demobbed, he remained in this country. Worked for Christie's, then set up shop on his own. He consistently outscored the auction houses and Agnew's in uncovering the whereabouts of all kinds of lost masterworks. Made his fortune doing that."

What a sluggard I've become, I tell myself. "I have forgotten the name, but do recall the career," I say.

Duval is mollified. "So you know what a key figure he was in the art world?"

I nod my head.

"Well, the fellow has been dead almost two years. A biography is much needed." Duval states this as if it were an irrefutable fact. "No one has yet stepped into the breach," he concludes without pausing.

My face must express doubt or disbelief, but Duval will have none of it.

"If there are lives of Kenneth Clark and Joseph Duveen, a much greater man such as Gabriel Brown must be similarly honoured." This he utters in an unabashedly patriotic manner, like Henry V giving his famous pep talk to his troops at Agincourt.

"In fact, Guy, we have been asked, under the most generous terms imaginable, to publish such a book within the next year." There is an inordinately long pause. "Mr. Carstairs and I have decided that this is the perfect project for you. You are custom made for it."

He informs me that Spoonbill was commissioned to produce this book by a group of devoted friends of Brown who have collected a substantial amount of money. "A very substantial amount," he emphasizes.

Spoonbill is also to find the most appropriate writer for the task. "We could have asked Holroyd or Tomalin, but Mr. Carstairs prefers a fresher face."

I interpret "fresher face" to mean one who will be available on the cheap due to desperate circumstances. Weakly, I demur: "I've never written a biography."

"Nonsense, old man. Biography is just fiction with a few rules thrown in. You'll take to it like a duck to water."

Having captured my full attention, Duval outlines the details of the proposed undertaking. The biography does not have to be long, perhaps only a hundred pages. It will be accompanied by reproductions, all in full colour, of one hundred of Gabriel Brown's most important "acquisitions." There is to be a full bibliography and a detailed index.

"A large amount of cash has been tossed our way. 120,000 pounds. I wanted to offer you 50,000, but Mr. Carstairs is a person of a more magnanimous disposition. 'Give the fellow 70,000,' he insisted. 'Tell him to quit his job and remind him that he must pay all his own travel expenses.'"

Carstairs is a man of infinite generosity.

"There it is, my dear chap."

Gulping is not the most elegant of reflex actions, but I cannot help myself.

Duval sees — as he must have hoped — that cupidity and amazement have taken control of me, and continues. "We need the book within a year. From this day forward, you must relentlessly — and I might add ruthlessly — commit yourself to this venture."

CHAPTER TWO

❧

A godsend! I have been liberated. Here is a chance to redeem myself. I have the opportunity — this is the word that comes to mind — to take my career as a writer in a new direction at a very good rate of pay.

That said, I wonder if it would be best all round to postpone the announcement of my new arrangements. My ex-wife will insist on being apprised of the financial details so that child support payments for my thirteen-year-old son, Jacob, can be upped.

Duval informs me that he will keep the matter under wraps. "Better this way. We can reserve all our resources for promoting the book when it's in press." He then advises me of the difficulties that will confront me in researching the biography. "Gabriel Brown retired fifteen years ago. There's almost no correspondence, business records, those sorts of thing. Most of your information will have to come from interviews."

He has the phone number of a Miss Bryant, the dealer's secretary-receptionist, to whom he left all of his worldly goods. Duval directs me to begin with her.

"You'll have to get her to spill the beans. Spice up your story. Sex is a necessary staple of the biographer's art. Neglect it at your peril."

BROWN'S LISTING IS one of the shortest in the massive *Who's Who* tome. Name, address, DOB, names of parents, education, the date his gallery opened. He was born in 1922, arrived in England in 1945, opened his gallery five years later, was a spectacular success, retired in 1997 at the age of seventy-five, and listed the activities of the last fifteen years of his life as gardening and reading.

Though the listing is perfunctory, it does provide the address of Brown's gallery: 12 Albemarle Street. I decide to give it a look before I ring Miss Bryant, taking the Tube to Green Park and walking the short distance.

Albemarle is a street I have never bothered to wander down. I know that the former home of Byron's publisher, John Murray, is at number 50, in a building covered with ugly white stucco. Somehow it does not seem a suitable place for the incineration of the poet's steamy, kiss-and-tell memoirs. Thomas Agnew & Sons at number 3, and the Parker Gallery opposite it, seem more appropriate neighbours for Gabriel Brown. Both galleries are models of discretion. Their windows each contain a single enticing work on display, behind which thick gauze conceals the interior. Agnew's is inhabited by a drunken Dutchman, a model of hearty geniality, painted by a "Follower of Franz Hals." The Parker has a large mezzotint of the expulsion of Adam and Eve, by John Martin. The two tiny figures are difficult to see amongst the terrifying but magnificent landscape bearing down on them.

To walk through the portals of either gallery one would need to have a high opinion of one's own chequebook, or a sang-froid that I do not possess. I might, in my new role, have to brave these establishments — but not today. Instead I scout the street, moving slowly up and down both sides, fully aware that in my anorak, jeans, and trainers I look a bit scruffy in comparison to my fellow window shoppers.

Number 12 is in the process of being transformed into a high-end sushi bar. Since Brown's time, it has been a spa, a luggage shop, and an antique store. The interior, stripped down for work to commence on its newest incarnation, is tiny. Brown's gallery would have been minute, especially in comparison to his competitors'. There is space for a showroom perhaps forty feet wide and fifty deep, and I can see that there had been a small private office at the very back. Hardly room enough to store anything. How could someone have made a fortune from such bare bones?

～

MISS BRYANT. I cannot help but imagine myself a young Pip, calling upon a reclusive, frowzy old gentlewoman living in a dilapidated cold-water flat in Bayswater. Perhaps there will be uneaten wedding cake on offer? A glass of madeira?

When I telephone her, she is cordial but reserved. "Of course. I'll be delighted to meet with you at your convenience. I am delighted that you have agreed to do the book. I have been assured that you are the perfect person for the job. Would you like to come here for coffee and then a stroll over to where Mr. Brown lived?"

No tea. Coffee? Miss Bryant is part of the New Britain, where

Starbucks, Caffè Nero, and Costa blanket the urban landscape. Perhaps everything is going to be, as my mother says, hunky-dory.

Should I purchase a recording device? Have plenty of pencils at the ready? Read Virginia Woolf's essay "The Art of Biography"? I decide against a machine, remembering a journalist friend telling me that such technology is counterproductive; often the interviewee will ask for the recorder to be shut off lest anything genuinely revealing be placed on record. When it comes to pencils, I am a perfect klutz; they self-destruct in my large, unwieldy fingers. And I recall that Woolf was not reckoned a distinguished life writer. In the end, I decide to rely on a ballpoint pen and my Filofax.

MISS BRYANT IS a small, slim woman, with a head of white hair carefully arranged in a bun. Her two-bedroom flat is in a 1930s building opposite Belsize Park Tube stop, with a sitting room overlooking the street. As I gaze out the window, she says, "This street is always bustling, sometimes noisy. I like to feel connected to other people."

Nothing is out of place in the room. On her mantelpiece are photographs of young people, likely nieces and nephews. I am surprised by the absence of artwork.

"Make yourself at home. You will have all sorts of questions for me about Gabriel," she observes matter-of-factly, as if she expects an interrogation to be imminent.

Startled, I assure her we can take our time, ease into the matter.

Miss Bryant nods. "I daresay you're correct."

She hands me three snapshots of Brown. One is from the 1950s, the others much more recent. He does not age much between them. Sandy hair, wonderfully proportioned nose and mouth, large sunken eyes. The smile is breathtaking in its expansiveness.

"He was a looker, no doubt about that," Miss Bryant points out. "Kept his looks too. And his perfect manners. That was what always captivated everyone. He exuded charm. Never heard him say a bad word about anyone, even under his breath. Always a smile on his face. Never knew anyone like him."

So Gabriel Brown was a paragon of virtue.

Aware of my skepticism, she continues. "I know what you must be thinking. 'She's the kind of woman who falls in love with her boss and comes to believe he can do no wrong.'" She takes a long pause. "That's not it. I'm not the kind of person to let anything get by me, especially over more than thirty years. A long, long time to idealize anyone. He would have fallen off his pedestal if I had constructed one. But he was exceptional."

I change the subject to seek information beyond the *Who's Who* listing. According to Miss Bryant, Brown began as a porter at Christie's in 1946, rising meteor-like to department head of Old Masters within three years. He was said to have a remarkable eye for that period, very much in the Bernard Berenson mould.

"Most of those paintings are unsigned. Very difficult to get anyone who can look at them and know within a matter of seconds who painted them. Men like Gabriel have some sort of internal hard drive. It was amazing to see him at work, how quickly he could determine everything there was to know about a canvas.

"About ten years ago, when Gabriel had been retired a few years, a huge double portrait canvas came up for sale at

Sotheby's. I was with him when he inspected the canvas. It was a painting of two ladies clad in Greek costume walking hand in hand, misty clouds behind them. The auction house's expert was certain the picture showed the great actress Mrs. Siddons with her niece Fanny Kemble — who later also enjoyed a successful career on the stage — and that the artist was almost certainly George Romney, who was known to have visited the two ladies in March 1828. As far as the expert was concerned, it was a done deal.

"Gabriel smiled warmly at him and told him neither woman bore the slightest resemblance to Siddons or Kemble. 'They had more refined, enchanting profiles. These two are presented well, but they don't have the poise that Romney customarily bestows. I also don't see any magic in this picture. I suspect the artist is someone who strayed from his usual appointed rounds.'

"Nonplussed, the expert said he would dig deeper. Two weeks later, he phoned Gabriel. Further research had been conducted: the two sisters were the Waldegraves, and the painter was Ozias Humphrey, the miniaturist."

If I am supposed to be impressed, I am. "Did Brown sell only Old Masters?"

"Yes and no. When he first opened his gallery, it was difficult to obtain good pieces. Remember he had to compete with the auction houses and firms like Agnew's to offer the best terms to a seller or convince a seller that he knew how to effectively market his picture. He once told me he started with Italian and French mannerists, which were in good supply in the late 1940s because they had not yet acquired any special kind of status. Then he got his hands on some early Italians, then some good French neo-classical wares by Poussin, and later he would offer the occasional Picasso or Matisse — the new Old Masters. I would say his sole criterion was quality. If he liked a picture well enough to sell it, or had someone in mind that might like it, he would snap it up. He was famous for buying low and selling high. That was the only way he could survive."

"Did he sell only paintings?"

"He told me that when he first started out he had a stock of master drawings. Never prints. When I began working for him in 1977, he sold only watercolours or oils — mostly oils."

"I wandered down to Albemarle the other day. I take it there were no storage facilities there?"

"Absolutely correct. When I show you his home, you'll see that there was a storage room there. Sold canvases were dispatched to their new homes on Mondays, when we were closed. On the same day, new ones were collected by lorries from his home and delivered to Albemarle."

Miss Bryant offers a choice of coffee, double espresso, or cappuccino, and is delighted when I select the espresso.

I am finding it difficult to know what to ask next. I need to know so much, but the scattergun approach to obtaining information isn't necessarily productive. I decide to press her about Brown's private life and see how far I can get.

"I knew Gabriel well, but he never confided in me," is her crisp reply. "His work was his life. He travelled a great deal in acquiring canvases. I took very few phone calls that were personal in nature."

"Did he ever talk about his life back in Canada, before he arrived here?"

"He mentioned being a student at University College in the University of Toronto. I think he read Modern Languages. Never mentioned any chums there."

"Surely he must have revealed something about his parents?"

A very sad smile crosses the lady's face. "I would have thought he would have mentioned them. Or the existence of a brother or sister. Not a single word."

Despite Miss Bryant's attempt to be helpful, my mind is inundated with anxiety-provoking thoughts. Do all biographical projects begin in such a void? As soon as I try to touch Gabriel Brown he flees, as if deliberately attempting to evade me. He remains a cipher even for a close associate like Miss Bryant. How can I possibly construct a coherent account of someone whose entire existence is a mystery?

CHAPTER THREE
𝕰𝕽

As we walk four blocks north towards Gabriel Brown's former home, Miss Bryant grows more forthcoming. She tells me Brown announced his intention to retire about twelve years before he died. He told her he had become increasingly queasy about dealing in pictures, and did not like the way the coming of the Internet had made some aspects of his profession obsolete. When he began his career, he was among a select group that both educated and edified the public. Now — incorrectly, in his view — most people were of the opinion that Googling could educate them in all the intricacies of art history. Very few so-called lovers of art really felt the importance of confronting pieces in museums or galleries. Even institutions such as the National Gallery and the Metropolitan had become inordinately dependent on peddling reproductions on greeting cards and calendars.

"'I am old and perhaps, as a result, disillusioned,' he said. 'I'm getting out.'"

Since Miss Bryant had worked for him for so many years,

he intended to purchase, on her behalf, an annuity that would pay her salary.

"It was typical of him to be bountiful," she insists. Embarrassed by such generosity, she told her employer she did not require any such assistance because she had inherited a great deal from her parents and he immediately agreed to drop the plan. Miss Bryant is still flummoxed by her inheritance, and does not know what she will do with all the money that has fallen in her lap. I suspect that she has provided the funding for the biography; she is my benefactress.

THE SMALL HOUSE on Malden Road is not, I feel, suitable for a person as grand as I imagine Gabriel Brown to have been. Still, the Georgian exterior — a modern reconstruction — embodies understated elegance, and the small front lawn is square and immaculate. I imagine the interior is filled with wonderful furnishings. Did Brown's taste venture towards eighteenth-century France or, because he was an immigrant to Britain, towards Chippendale and other great English masters? How many wonderful pieces of Chinoiserie will there be on display?

As soon as we enter the foyer, however, I am thrown into confusion. The two large rooms on either side of the staircase — a sitting room and a dining room — are painted in the palest of beiges. The furniture and accessories are by contemporaries of Alvar Aalto. Not even the works of art on the wall — all master prints by twentieth-century modernists including Munch, Picasso, Matisse, and Cézanne — can relieve the sleek Nordic modernism.

Miss Bryant allows a slight smile to manifest itself. "You're surprised?"

"I would have thought Brown's home would be done in a grand style. Neo-classical, or even baroque or rococo. What I see startles me."

"Gabriel always maintained that he did not like to take his work home with him. He also said that he did not have the money to collect Old Masters. I suspect he found the prints an acceptable compromise."

As we wander the downstairs, I am struck by its rigid good taste. There is nothing really comfortable about the place; I cannot imagine it as a restful environment, as a place of refuge. It is too much like a museum.

Miss Bryant seems adept at reading my thoughts. "I understand your disappointment. Let's take a look at the sitting room at the back. He called it a den."

She points me in the direction of the small state-of-the-art kitchen that looks like it has never been used. In the room behind it, overlooking the garden, is the kind of interior I had envisioned: comfortable, stuffed furniture, a James Adams-style mantelpiece, a few small pieces of Georgian furniture. A huge modernist desk stands in the centre of the den, and bookcases fill three walls. Strangely for this day and age, there is no sign of a computer. The space would have offered a retreat from the rest of the house.

"This room was the nerve centre," Miss Bryant observes. "Gabriel spent most of his time here."

The tour is not yet complete. We move to the two bedrooms upstairs. The smaller one, with a single bed, dressing table, and wardrobe, had been Brown's; the other space, which ordinarily would have been used for a master bedroom, had instead been reserved for the storing of canvases. That room is now eerily empty; our voices reverberate harshly within it. I breathe deeply — perhaps too deeply.

"You feel overwhelmed. I thought such feelings might seize you. It makes what I am about to propose difficult." Miss Bryant turns to face me. "Mr. Duval has mentioned to me your reduced circumstances in life. Perhaps, for the year you are writing the biography, you should move here? I am in no hurry to sell the house. Come and go as you please. If you inhabit these walls, perhaps through a kind of osmosis you will come to know Gabriel better."

The smile that illuminates her face has no irony in it, and I realize she is a well-meaning soul. She adores Brown and wishes for me to take after her.

Normally my response would be dictated by something squalidly self-centred, in this particular case the urgency of making and perhaps saving money — but these aren't the sentiments that allow me to accept the offer. Though I do not wish to live here on Malden Road, I have to dedicate myself to the project that has been thrust my way. I want to know Gabriel Brown in order to write about him.

I decide to camp out in the den. The aloofness of the rest of the house chills me. I place my laptop on the desk and wonder if by doing so I am desecrating Brown's sanctuary.

CHAPTER FOUR

❧

My son, Jacob, is lavish in his praise of my new digs. He does not see that modernist rooms such as these fail to provide a comfortable living space. Instead he notices that they are filled on a sunny day with pure, bright light. The sharp, angular lines and pale colours cause the house to-tingle with an energy he responds to. I try to follow his lead.

Jacob moves solemnly from print to print, his small green eyes transfixed. He informs me that he can draw as well as Miró, and offers to provide a demonstration. Chagall's red and purple moons and blue floating horses make him laugh. He is amazed by the two Rauschenberg combines.

He tells me that he wishes he could have met Mr. Brown, but does not tell me why. Children usually do not like to tell adults the whys behind their preferences.

When I press him on the issue, he shrugs his shoulders and offers a hard-to-fathom explanation: "He must have been a fun-loving person."

Fun-loving is not my response to the elusive Gabriel Brown.

Though I have little reason to feel ungrateful or chary of the man who is putting bread on my table, I remain wary.

⌒

I HAVE BEEN given a small number of names and addresses. Since I have to begin somewhere, I decide to approach the first: Vivien Hampton.

About her, Miss Bryant is the soul of discretion. "She was one of Gabriel's friends when he first arrived here. I think they saw a great deal of each other for a while." I note a definite emphasis on *saw* and *for a while*. In other words, the two were an item and then went their separate ways. Or am I reading too much into her words?

As it turns out, I have decoded the signs correctly. Miss Hampton is startled when I phone her. "A biography of Gabriel Brown? What a strange undertaking! It's not as if his is a house-hold name."

"I apologize for being involved in such a dubious enterprise. Some of his friends want a memorial volume. A commemoration."

"He was a well-known dealer. I would think the matter begins and ends there. The world is overpopulated with books — as well as people."

I readily agree in an attempt to get her on side — but then ask if, in this instance, she might be willing to assist me.

"I'd have to think the matter through. I knew Gabriel quite well a number of years ago. I'm not sure I want to revisit that time, especially as I'm not sure I approve of what you're doing. I've reached a time in my life when I do not wish to remember certain parts of the past." She possesses a husky voice, the kind that retains its sultry tone, and the line sounds rehearsed, thrown away in a Joan Crawford manner. "I guess it wouldn't hurt if we met briefly to talk about my old companion. I'm not sure I can remember very much. I'm in my eighties, you know. Lots of the past — especially the Hitler War — have vanished from memory. Gone AWOL."

She laughs at her own joke, the starchiness still in her voice, and we agree to meet the following week.

GABRIEL BROWN HAS not left a proper archive behind. Since he apparently did not own or even know how to use a computer, there is no hard drive to examine. No letters to him of any kind have survived.

There are, however, a few invoices for catalogue subscriptions from the auction houses. There are also a few small leather-bound journals, each filled with enigmatic jottings such as these:

TOKYO/LEWIS/LLS
ROTTERDAM/BRUNONI/SK

I have no context into which to fit these.

And then there are ledger books in black buckram, with more difficult-to-decipher entries — though there are some relatively easy ones:

LEONARDO DRAWING — 12 JANUARY 1977
£85,000
DUKE OF NORTHUMBERLAND: £225,000 — 5 AUGUST 1989

I take this notation to signify that Brown purchased a Leonardo at a relatively low price in 1977, held on to it for twelve years, then sold it for a much higher amount. Miss Bryant tells me that despite the high rent on Albemarle, the profits made were astronomical. She informs me, in genteel language, that a good dealer buys in at the cheapest possible price and then screws a wealthy client out of a higher sum. She also reveals that she never dealt with accounts. "Gabriel did all that work at home."

Then there are more complicated notations:

SCHOOL OF GAINSBOROUGH — 14 JANUARY 1990
£150,000 CHRISTIE'S
RESTORATION AND RE-FRAMING: £50,000
EARL OF GOTHAM — £1,000,000 — 3 MARCH 1993

That markup seems excessive, even compared to the Leonardo drawing. Wouldn't the nobleman have balked at paying such an enormous sum for a canvas he could have bought for a relatively small sum a few years before? The picture must have, in the ensuing years, been firmly attributed to the master, no longer a "School of" piece.

I'm beginning to understand that even the rich are at the mercy of the vagaries of history — and of conniving dealers.

∽

I AM SEEING more and more of Miss Bryant. Although I quiz my new acquaintance in pursuit of facts, we soon grow comfortable in each other's company and come to enjoy our chats.

She does not so much worship Brown as venerate him. She

conceives of him as a person who embodied the very finest attributes of someone in his trade: "He knew how to talk to people in the nicest possible way"; "he was respectful of the aristocracy and the rich, but he made it clear that he had knowledge and expertise from which they were closeted"; "he was an excellent salesperson, someone who was well aware that he was selling top goods." She will have none of my hints that Gabriel Brown might have been overly manipulative of his clients.

About herself, Miss Bryant becomes more revealing. She was born in Wiltshire to a wealthy family who felt that girls did not require rooms of their own, much less university educations. She remained with her parents until they died, then sold the family home and moved to London.

"I'm an arts aficionado. Cinema, art exhibitions, opera, ballet, books. London is the perfect place for me. I began working for Gabriel because I needed to occupy my weekdays." She wishes to know more about me, and on this topic is direct: "I am anxious to learn what makes you tick."

At first I am not comfortable with the tables being turned against me, but my reserve soon vanishes. Like everyone I know, I enjoy talking about myself.

"According to my parents, I was — when they were feeling modest — an *early bloomer*. That probably hits the nail on its head, but the metaphor pales in comparison to how my parents imagined me. When I was five years old I remember being trotted out as if I were the Christ Child being taken to the Temple by Mary and Joseph. *Adults are always surprised that such a wee creature knows so much* was their frequent refrain. When I did well in school, and later at Oxford, my successes were outlandishly praised. Everything I did was a cause for celebration. To be honest, I got spoiled for real life. Mum and Dad are the same about Jacob. That scares me a bit. I don't want him ending up like his old man."

"I don't think that would be such a bad thing," Miss Bryant assures me.

"I married early. Stella was at St. Hilda's. Her background is similar to mine. Middle of the middle class. Parents pushed her from the get-go. We decided to settle in London. She got work as a temp but within two years she was the PA to Sir Joseph Adams, the media mogul. I was not so fortunate until you came along. I used to be ambitious about my writing. If you listen to my mother, she'll tell you I'm the next Flaubert."

"And are you?"

"More like Flaubert's parrot. Dirty and mangy."

She laughs politely.

"I began as a trainee-manager at Waterstone's, and discovered that I was very good at my job. I came to enjoy it. A lot of the time all I had to do was answer simple questions. But then there were the die-hards, the people actually interested in books, some of whom actually enjoyed talking with someone with similar proclivities. Quite often I came across a person with interests completely different from mine, and I asked them for reading suggestions.

"I bought more books than I sold. Even with my discount, these purchases added up. Stella became more and more infuriated, eventually rage-filled. 'You spend all day wasting your time talking with customers, and you actually listen to what they have to say. That's not your job. You're supposed to be working for a profit-making enterprise. Not spending your time wanking.'

"After Jacob arrived, Stella felt she could not take time off. 'We'll land up in the Marshalsea. I think that's what you hoity-toity literary types call debtor's prison.' So I took a year off work instead. Jacob liked the arrangement. So did I. He became the centre of my existence. Then I returned to work. Stella found Geoff. And I wound up in solitary splendour in Crickle-wood. All in all, my life lacks highlights."

"Such is existence for most of us," Miss Bryant says. "From now on, you are to call me Amelia. No more of this Miss Bryant business."

Chapter Five

𝄞

I hope my meeting with Vivien Hampton can help me unearth the pinnacles of achievement that constituted Brown's life.

Hampton's emerald green eyes and ivory skin, grazed with light freckling, betray the fact that she once had auburn hair — a prized inheritance that has faded over time. Lest anyone doubt her original hue, she has chemically enhanced it to carrot red. She softens this by placing her hair in a chignon of the style favoured by women in the Fifties. Her nose and lips are finely and elegantly curved. She has retained a girlish figure, and at about six feet stands taller than me. Obviously a heavy smoker, Hampton banishes the evidence of her addiction with a heavy floral spray, the chemical equivalent of lilies of the valley. Unfortunately, the combination of the two smells is not a happy one, bringing out the worst excesses of each; the resulting sickly sweet scent clots the air.

Hampton takes pleasure in contrivance. Her flat, near Lord's on Regent's Park Road, is far removed from the twenty-first century. The sitting room contains so many teak bookcases, end tables, chairs, and settees that a visitor could be excused for thinking they are in Oslo or Copenhagen. The seven or eight huge vases in the room, with their deliberately mismatched colors, are 1950s Poole — the work of Alfred Read, who, I recall, was influenced by Swedish design. I have always found stuffed Scandinavian furniture a challenge to sink into. That conviction is reinforced when I try to settle myself, at my hostess's insistence, into her sofa.

Hampton inspects me carefully, her jewel-like eyes narrowed and penetrating. She seems a person who never suffers fools under any circumstances, and I am not sure she likes what she beholds.

A small smile crosses her face, and she breaks the silence. "I have been asking myself if Gabriel would approve of my talking to you." She pauses for a few seconds. "Since he has no choice in the matter, I must make my own decision. I resolved to take a look at your books, all three of which I bought at the Waterstone's around the corner last week."

If she notices the panic that overwhelms me, she takes no notice.

"They are fine books. The work of a sensitive person. They helped me decide I can trust you."

Only now does Hampton ask if I would like something to drink. I ask for a coffee, and she strolls into the kitchen and emerges with a tray and two large mugs. She pushes one in my direction and tells me to help myself to milk and sugar.

"I met Gabriel in 1946, in this very room, when I was twenty-one. I had been in London for three years then; I'd had a good war working in a typing pool in the Ministry of

Information. By 'a good war' I mean that despite spending five dull days a week cooped up in an office, I partied an average of three or four nights. There was always the risk of a bomb taking one's life away, but I enjoyed the danger. I discovered that my pleasure increased in accordance with the amount of peril I confronted. I even liked the rubble that filled the streets. I suppose that it is an odd thing to confess about oneself."

"You were aware that you might lose your life," I offer. "Therefore, you did everything in your power to enjoy it."

"Well put. In any event, you want to know about my relationship with Gabriel. Everything else is irrelevant."

I interrupt her. "I need to understand you in order to write about your friendship with Brown. Anything you might wish to tell me is of interest."

"For a young person, you are remarkably considerate. Your mother must be proud of you."

She tells me about her family's grand home in Dorset, her education there, her decision at the age of eighteen to do her bit for the war effort. Her parents were shocked by her resolve to live in the metropolis, which they considered a breeding ground for all kinds of depravity. But she was adamant, so they insisted that if she were to move to London she would take over the family flat in Regent's Park Road, previously used only when Mr. Hampton travelled on business.

"Another Canadian brought Gabriel to my flat. There were a great many Canadians in London during, and especially after, the war. In 1946, most of these men were waiting for transport back to Canada. Sometimes soldiers had to wait a long time for a ship to carry them back.

"You will know from photographs that Gabriel was exceptionally tall. He was handsome, had a very good physique, and carried himself well. To my mind, he never wandered into a room — he cut through it. I was attracted to him because he was, in many ways, an extraordinary person. He laughed a lot. He was a man who never had to make an effort to appear manly. In my experience, that's unusual. We became lovers the night we met." She clears her throat and continues. "Our physical relationship was good."

Hampton abruptly changes the subject. "If you want to understand Gabriel, you must take into account that he revered everything English. He took pleasure in the simplest things. The way we say 'lorry' instead of 'truck,' for instance.

"Among my friends, he became known as The Canadian. I think that made him wince a bit, although he realized the nickname was meant affectionately. For them, to be Canadian was synonymous with being open, friendly, and compassionate."

I realize my duty as a biographer requires me to probe further, into areas Hampton might not wish for me to venture, such as what their relationship had been like, and why it had come to an end. But I am not sure how to raise these issues.

Hampton herself takes the plunge into murky waters. "I suppose you want to know what went wrong between us? "

I hope my ears are not perking up too much. "I would be most grateful," I respond deferentially.

"Well. He could discourse on a wide range of subjects, and give anyone he was with the impression that they were the most important person in the world. Positively clung to everything they said. But at the time, I was convinced that Gabriel would never marry anyone — and, unfortunately, time has proven me right. He was an extremely outgoing person — except."

"Except?"

"Except when talking about his feelings. They were forbidden territory."

"Women often make that complaint about men."

"Comes with the gender. But Gabriel would not make the slightest attempt to make his personal thoughts on anything known. If I attempted to penetrate his real self, he became silent. His easy smile vanished."

"Do you think he had a secret?"

"Yes. One day, in a rare introspective moment, he compared himself to a phoenix raised from the ashes. He looked me directly in the eye and said, 'In coming to England, I've been reborn.' But he did not provide any details. I am convinced his secret is something in his past, something that happened in Canada. He hardly ever spoke of Canada. If I pressed him, he might regale me with trivia, such as the fact that Yonge Street in Toronto had a very tawdry section and was the longest street in the world. But he brushed aside any questions about his parents, about his upbringing."

"So you quarreled?"

"Not really. Gabriel wouldn't even go that far. The more time I spent with him, the more of a cipher he became. I could only see his surface. Not much upon which to build a relationship. We began to see each other less and less. Then neither of us made a phone call.

"I more or less followed his meteoric rise by seeing photographs of him over the years in the paper. Gabriel never seemed to age, very much like Dorian Gray. I have sometimes wondered: did he have a portrait stored away somewhere that recorded his real self? Just an old woman's musings, I suppose."

I FEEL SORRY for myself. Most biographers have plenty of facts about their subjects, sometimes so many that it is difficult to sort out the trivial from the significant. But then there are subjects like Jane Austen, about whom there remains a paucity of details. In such cases, there is the temptation to read too much into the little that is known. Why did the celebrated novelist accept a proposal of marriage one evening and then, over breakfast the next day, inform the bloke that there was no deal? Did she have a sleepless night, tossing and turning over abandoning her spinsterhood? Did she fear being subject to the whims of a man? Did she know she was too clever for this fellow? Or did she want to marry but knew he was not the right person? Did she have an old lover lodged in the back — or front — of her mind?

My problems seem relatively simple in comparison to the dilemmas facing Austenites. However, I am still dealing with a man who seems to have had such a shallow emotional life — or was so wounded that he did everything to hide it — that it might be impossible to uncover the personality residing behind the mask.

~

THREE YEARS AGO, I purchased a number of Lego sets for Jacob. I opened each box with a great deal of panache, beheld hundreds of variously coloured plastic bits, and became overwhelmed with panic. Jacob looked up at me beaming, but the look of rapture on his small face did not comfort me. How was I going to deal with the jumble in front of me? Slowly, awkwardly, painfully, I went from step to step, until a recognizable form emerged. Though Lego manuals are illustrated in such a way as to give comfort to the most challenged of fathers, I made many mistakes along each of these journeys. I often had to undo what I had done and stumble forward again to exhaustedly reach the finish line. I always had extra pieces left at the end.

"Daddy, Lego gives you the exact number of pieces required," was the only reproach Jacob ever made. And though I grinned idiotically, his look of adoration remained intact.

Nowadays, father worship has vanished from my son's relationship to me. Long gone too are the days when I was afraid to touch newborn Jacob lest he break. Those wonderful, tender moments of being at one with him are a distant memory. Jacob is in the process of becoming his own person.

I purchase much more complex and larger boxes of Lego for him now. When I offer to assist, he politely demurs; a slight smile crosses his face, a child's version of a scoff. He knows the Lego world is not one I comfortably inhabit. He opens the box, flips through the manual in twenty seconds, and proceeds to produce a spaceship in about fifteen minutes. There is never an unused piece.

Two weeks ago, Jacob told me of a plan he and his friend Ralph, who accompanies him on his stays with me at Brown's home, had devised. They intend to undo a slew of completed Lego sets and merge them together into a large construction of their own design. I applaud their ingenuity.

"You never go into the front sitting room," he says. "Can we work there?" He is pleased when I agree, and names a further stipulation: this "sculpture" — his word — of Lego will take a long time to make, be extremely tall, perhaps as high as five feet, and is to remain a secret until completed.

Not wishing to be an enemy of the arts, I agree to supply a sheet that will cover the work in progress from prying eyes — including mine — and volunteer to absent myself from the room when the two are working. One moonlit evening, I walk into the room. At the very centre, I see that the sheet covering the sculpture has risen higher and higher as construction progresses. It almost looks like a ghost is presiding over the Wassily chairs, the Eileen Gray side tables, and the Barcelona chairs. I wonder if this is the closest I am ever going to get to Brown.

~

MY OLD SCHOOL pal, William, is a hack for hire who has recently done a "quickie" biography of Proust, an ebook that succinctly conveys Marcel's life history in one hundred pages. Though he squeezed a three-week all-expenses-paid stay in Paris — "to soak up local colour" — out of the venture, he did not enjoy the writing experience.

"I used to think Proust was a genius. I was only seventeen when I devoured *À la recherche du temps perdu.* My whole adolescent worldview was wrapped up in those books. Then, last year I researched the fellow's life. Nothing much happened. He sometimes got his rocks off by watching two caged rats kill each other. He took wanking to a whole new level."

William has a succinct, if crude, way of expressing himself, but I see his point. Who wants to invest time in another person's life, only to discover that the object of his pursuit bores or repulses him?

Chapter Six

A melia has more than once called my attention to the fact that Gabriel Brown had a gift for words. I encounter little evidence to support this claim, until I recall that among Brown's notebooks is an elaborately printed pamphlet he had authored in 1975. That year, a select exhibit was held at a small gallery room at the Royal Academy to commemorate Brown's twenty-fifth anniversary as a dealer. Six canvases he had sold during his career were borrowed back from their owners — the National Gallery in London, the Prado, the Louvre, the Metropolitan, the National Gallery in Washington, and a gentleman from Japan — for the exhibit. Amelia recalls that the canvases were so valuable no assurance company would insure them if they were shown on Albemarle Street.

The pamphlet, bound in green morocco and printed on vellum, collects Brown's writings on those six portraits, which he felt represented the apex of his achievement as a dealer. Could I discover any evidence of Brown, the man, in these pieces?

FOREWORD

I have had the great good fortune to deal in fine art for the past twenty-five years and cannot think of a more pleasant way to spend one's time. I have had enormous pleasure in being constantly surrounded by beautiful things, and these wondrous objects have repaid me over and over again for the time I have spent in their company.

Many canvases have passed through my hands, but my most fortunate finds have been portraits. I include the six ladies and gentlemen assembled here among my closest friends. In each case, I have spent long hours in his or her presence, gotten to know each well, and wept when he or she travelled to a new home. In this exhibition, they are reunited. Look into their eyes carefully, and you will behold the whole of human existence: joy, sorrow, exaltation, happiness, fear. The full gamut of the comic and the tragic are readily discernible in these countenances. Each of them is a masterpiece of the portraitist's art.

Chi saggiamente e ben	*If you wish to paint Love*
Vuole dipingere Amore	*Wisely and well,*
Il tenga prima in sen	*You better hold him in your heart.*
Ch'ogni pittori alfin	*For a painter will fail*
Perde l'opra e 'l colore	*To draw and colour him properly*
Se non l'ha si vicin.	*If he is not living in his heart.*

SANDRO BOTTICELLI

PORTRAIT OF
AN UNKNOWN YOUNG WOMAN

TEMPERA ON PANEL

49 X 37 CM

CIRCA 1475

THE METROPOLITAN MUSEUM OF ART, NEW YORK CITY

This mesmerizing portrait represents the high point in this artist's career as a portraitist. A young woman is shown against a bright background. Her blondish tresses, blue eyes, and upturned nose are characteristic of this artist's finest work.

This young lady has learned the value of charm. She sets out to beguile the onlooker. This woman may be aloofly and elegantly beautiful, but she has deliberately removed herself from ordinary human existence. She finds comfort only within herself.

There is a remnant of fear in the deepest part of her soul, but she does not wish to display that emotion lest she be destroyed by it. This is a person who has learned the value of reticence. Nevertheless, her eyes are filled with a passionate longing for something that has been snatched away.

LEONARDO DA VINCI

PORTRAIT OF A BOY

OIL ON WOOD
34 X 20 CM
CIRCA 1494
THE PRADO, MADRID

The sitter is androgynous. His eyes are tear-filled, his expression languid, his upper lip swollen. Rarely has the psychology of an individual been so nakedly rendered.

The eyes ravish the viewer. It is as if the boy had kept them firmly closed and, of a sudden, opened them. He searches the viewer for certainty. Will you take care of me? Do I matter to you? He is aware he is a person of great beauty, but genuine fear and worry crisscross his face. This youngster has endured some deep loss and is unsure of how to recover from that suffering. The certainty he seeks from the viewer is the assurance that he will not be again victimized.

Nature must have been dismayed that a mortal like Leonardo could have revealed her secrets so precisely and elegantly. The sitter is one of the most perfect examples of the portraitist's art ever seen.

HANS HOLBEIN THE YOUNGER

PORTRAIT OF A NOBLE YOUNG MAN

Oil and tempera on wood
76 x 51 cm
Circa 1520
The National Gallery, Washington

This red-haired, blue-eyed man is richly dressed in a coat with fur lapels. His remarkable composure and strong masculine features belie the overall impression that he is extremely young.

One thing of which we can be certain is that this man relishes worldly success. He is perfectly aware that life is a masquerade. One must always have one's mask firmly in place lest one's vulnerability be revealed. To be honest is to be ravaged. One must play the game properly, even if it involves cheating.

He will achieve more money and more power. In fact, he will obtain everything upon which he sets his sights. His recessed, dark brown eyes assure us of this.

REMBRANDT HARMENSZOON VAN RIJN

PORTRAIT OF A STREET VAGRANT

OIL ON CANVAS
105 X 76 CM
CIRCA 1641
THE LOUVRE

The melancholia of everyday life inhabits those deep black eyes. There is no corner of unhappiness this woman of the underclass has not witnessed. She is indigent, completely destitute, and in poor health. Yet despite all encumbrances, she soldiers on. She has no other choice.

This woman is not physically pleasing. Her features, large and distended, melt gracelessly into one another. Animal-like she covets life, but existence has not even a modicum of relief or pleasure to offer her.

JOHANNES VERMEER

PORTRAIT OF A WOMAN OF QUALITY

OIL ON CANVAS
46 X 40 CM
CIRCA 1665
PRIVATE COLLECTION, JAPAN

This wealthy woman looks beguilingly at the viewer. Her smile is open and easy. Life may be a sham, but she has learned how to navigate it. It has given her all she wants. She has learned the value of worldly pleasure.

Porcelain and the finest textiles are her material comforts for accepting the status quo. She is a realist. No romantic illusions about love on this earth, or the one beyond, interrupt her reflections. Steadily she looks at the world. If this portrait is read symbolically, it would be titled *Pragmatism*.

This is an unusual picture in Vermeer's extremely small oeuvre. The smile of the lady does not seem entirely natural, does not radiate from inner goodness. Rather, it seems to be the construction of the sitter. The look on her face gestures in the direction of a smirk. The smile of the woman is so radically dissimilar from those seen in Vermeer's work that there has been some suggestion it is a fake. But the gentle brushwork and soft application of colours that is the preserve of this great painter clearly establishes the genuineness of this canvas.

JOSHUA REYNOLDS

PORTRAIT OF LADY RAYBURN AS ST. CECILIA

OIL ON CANVAS

239 X 147.5 CM

CIRCA 1752-53

THE NATIONAL GALLERY, LONDON

This woman appears before us in two guises. In the first, she is the wife of an Earl. She has married well above her station because her parents, the Brown family, had money but no prestige. The marriage is an alliance of convenience into which the lady has been forced by the aspirations of her mother and father.

In the second she is the patron saint of music, the woman who, as she lay dying, sang to God. This Cecilia is defiant. She does not allow any fear of death to inhabit her countenance.

The lady's full smile betrays everything. It is too wide, altogether too stretched. She is a parvenu who has made it to the very top of the English aristocracy. She can rest on her laurels, but she is not certain the battle was worth fighting.

In this full-scale portrait, Cecilia looks down at us. We cannot help but be moved. As a Saint, she inspires us to emulate her attachment to the divine. As a person, she is tormented by her stay on this earth.

BROWN'S PROSE IS clipped but elegant. His obvious love for the pieces is evident. Clearly, he found the correct vocation as a dealer.

I am beginning to suspect Brown was something of a romantic. His observations about the portraits are more than a bit cheerless, written by someone possessing firsthand knowledge of unmet expectations.

Brown also observes that, instead of astonishment or surprise, the six faces display fear. I am not so sure they do, yet he emphasizes that emotion. Is this a further clue to understanding him?

> *About suffering they were never wrong,*
> *The Old Masters: how well they understood.*
> *Its human position ...*

Gabriel Brown could easily have inserted W. H. Auden's lines into his brief catalogue. Perhaps I should use them as the epigraph to my biography?

WHEN I CASUALLY mention my impression of the pamphlet to Amelia, she looks me full in the face and says, "Guy Boyd, you are arriving at a wonderful understanding of Gabriel."

She begins to share fond memories of tipping each of the colour plates into the one-hundred-fifty copies of the small catalogue. "A labour of love, that was. Everything had to be perfect: the paper, the plates, the binding. They cost a good whack. That small exhibition room at the Academy was repainted pale lavender. We had a lot of expenses, plus a hefty rental."

I decide not to allow her to change the subject. "Why do you think I am beginning to know Gabriel Brown?"

"Gabriel liked that piece of verse by Auden. He had such a keen sense of the fragility of all human life, of how most things turn out badly. He once remarked that so much of life takes place quietly, or even secretly, while others are not looking."

CHAPTER SEVEN

M y next interview is with tall, sallow-eyed William Bendix, a preeminent dealer in Old Masters who has been plying his trade for more years than he cares to remember.

"Pictures," he enunciates in a very long drawl, "have been a part of my life since infancy. If one is to the manor born, there is no other way." This state of affairs seems to both please and perplex him. "I've never known anything else. The same goes for my father. I am the third generation of a family that has consecrated itself to art."

He laughs, making sure I have taken his point.

"I don't mean that picture-selling is a sacred profession. Nothing of the sort. But it's something that you must devote your entire life to. If you don't, you come away empty handed. Gabriel would have agreed with me. He devoted his entire life to his profession."

"He wasn't, however, to the manor born?" I ask.

"Maybe not. But he had an intuitive understanding of what we do, of the sacrifices we must make."

I look around his spacious office. Various etchings, lithographs, and small canvases occupying virtually all flat surfaces. "But it is a lucrative calling."

"That's as may be," Bendix concedes. "If you do it well, it takes all your time, eats it all up. And then, in the end, it can spit you out."

I'm not sure that I buy into Bendix's self-serving evaluation of a profession that continues to make him a rich man.

He seems to understand my dilemma. "If you sell high-end pictures, you have to spend a great deal of time unearthing them. If you don't, someone else will find them, and you're out of luck."

"But surely a lot of clients come to you with valuable pictures because of your family's reputation?"

"That's true. But such opportunities have always been few and far between. If I do my job correctly, I have to make things happen."

"Would you say the same was true for Brown?"

"Absolutely. Even more so. He started from scratch."

"What made him successful?"

"The easy answer? He was amiable, polite, and good looking. A born salesman. Knew his subject backwards and forwards, was never pushy. With aristos and landed gentry, Gabriel's impeccable manners were seductive. He wore the best shirts, suits, and ties. In that regard, he was extremely English. He actually believed in pomp, circumstance, hope, and glory. His love of all things English was, in my opinion, highly unrealistic. But when people witness such sincerity, they are beguiled. I could never hope to be so upbeat in dealing with clients.

"Gabriel was the complete Anglophile, but to my surprise he never lost his Canadian accent. Most people from Canada or Australia will, over the course of time, allow their way of speaking to sound English. Gabriel never did. And his accent may also have been a considerable asset. Sometimes we English are suspicious of our own. Many persons would have gotten in touch with Gabriel because of what he wasn't. This includes the German, the Spanish, and especially the French, who are reluctant to deal with Englishmen.

"I could proffer these reasons — excuses — to explain why Gabriel beat so many of us native Londoners at our game. But that would not be fair. He read all the books and catalogues and travelled widely in pursuit of finds. Did his homework better than most. He was diligent and hard·working; he did not have a lazy bone in his body. Above all, he was a risk taker. Must have been burnt badly a few times."

"Is that the reason his mark-ups were so high?" I venture to ask.

"So are mine!" Bendix responds. "Sometimes we have pictures in stock for many years before we find a buyer. It's an expensive proposition and we're always hedging our bets. Crazy not to."

I ask Bendix if there are any questions I have forgotten to ask.

"You're new at this biography business," he observes. "You're probably doing better than you think. The only other thing I can share with you is that I was quite surprised to discover the distance he put between himself and his native land. I don't think he ever returned there. Once upon a time — must have been twenty years ago — Brown and I were at a meeting at the Tate, where it was mentioned that the National Gallery of Canada in Ottawa was holding a John Martin exhibition. I don't know if you know his work. Huge, sublime landscapes overshadowing the human figures that inhabit them. Someone suggested Gabriel might wish to cross the pond to speak about them. A look of absolute horror crossed his face, and he made it abundantly clear that any such journey was out of the question. His vehemence surprised me. Not like him to let loose the reins of composure."

Chapter Eight

Three long months have passed. I have interviewed all the dealers, collectors, and friends of Gabriel Brown. They all recall the same impressions: Not a bad bloke. A bit reserved.

My relationship with Jacob has improved enormously. Stella texts me constantly to complain about how the house I am living in "rent-free" is having a bad influence on him, how his demands for more Lego pieces have become exorbitant. Ralph's mother has complained to Stella about her son's similar requests.

"Does his time with you have to be so costly?" she whines.

But what really enrages my ex-wife is that my son goes through every week with her looking forward to the weekend with Dad. This new state of affairs is, for her, revolutionary — in every bad sense of that word.

In addition to making their mysterious sculpture even larger, he and Ralph have taken to drawing. The boys have become neo-Cubists. They have asked permission to remove two of the Picassos from the wall so that they may scrutinize them more carefully, and are also working their way through Brown's heavily annotated 1930 edition of Helen Gardner's *Art Through the Ages.*

Jacob finds all five of Patricia Highsmith's *Ripley* books in the den, next to the complete set of Hergé's *Adventures of Tintin.* "What are those books about, Dad?" he asks. Though I tell him that Tom Ripley is a reprehensible con artist who emigrates from the United States to Europe, I give him permission to read the books. I also suggest he not mention the matter to his mother.

A week later, Jacob reveals that he has become a great admirer of Ripley. I consider myself a tolerant person, but I am shocked. My son identifies with a psychopath? Down what kind of garden path have I set his young feet?

Jacob, glimpsing my loosened jaw, responds, "Ripley is an orphan who learns how to make his way in the world."

"But he's a liar and a murderer."

"Yeah. But it's only a book. And he's really cool."

I decide it might be in my best interest to suggest Jacob read Brown's collection of le Carré. The morals there are not quite as dubious as in Highsmith.

What kind of ethical values is Jacob imbibing? In a few short weeks, he has graduated from comic book adventure stories to full-scale tales of betrayal and forgery.

∼

AMELIA AND I have become friends. I am fairly certain that she is providing Duval with glowing reports on my progress, since I have not heard from him in some time. For better or worse, she is a loyal person. Just as she remains deeply attached to

Gabriel Brown, she has also become a steadfast coadjutor to me. I can certainly be candid with her about my struggles with this project; she does not mind the role of sounding board.

"I have cast away the distance between my subject and myself," I confess. "I feel partial to him. There are very few people about whom no one utters a bad word."

"You feel you are acting unprofessionally?"

"To a degree. I don't think bonding between biographer and biographee is necessarily a good thing. But what really worries me is the scarcity of hard facts I have uncovered. I do not understand what made Brown tick."

"Perhaps you'll only discover that when you actually sit down and write out what you know?"

In that spirit, and recalling Duval's command that I establish my own unique take on Brown, I decided to try my hand at a sample chapter.

CHAPTER NINE
☙

Gabriel Brown: 1945–1966

Gazing down from the steps of Canada House, Gabriel could see the whole of Trafalgar Square. Nelson's column, the National Gallery, and St. Martin's were all bathed in soft afternoon light. It was difficult to imagine that until ten days ago the square was a prime target for enemy action: school children fed the pigeons; touts sold souvenirs; nannies and their small charges soaked in the warm air; secretaries strolled through on their lunch breaks; businessmen took shortcuts. The English had survived a severe test of courage, had endured through sheer force of will and grim determination. Bloodied but unbowed, London maintained its routines even among the most abject circumstances. This was the England Gabriel had read about in Dickens and Buchan.

He was visiting Canada House in order to enter his name in the lottery that would give him space on a returning ship. It was May, and he had arrived just in time to be demobbed. He had missed the war.

Later that night, he joined the throng dancing in the floodlit square. He didn't jump into the fountains or climb lampposts, but he was part of the conga line that wended its way to Buckingham Palace. He later told friends he had glimpsed among his fellow revelers Princess Elizabeth and Princess Margaret.

AFTER THAT GLORIOUS day and night in the Square, Gabriel — still, as he later put it, "VE Day-drunk" — decided he would find a way to remain in England. Canada was the child, England the mother. He would be the dutiful son who stayed at his mother's side. He wasn't remaining behind, he assured himself: he was returning home. In any event, he had no ties back in Toronto, no one awaiting his return. He would not be deserting anyone.

Gabriel decided he had the strong inner reserves needed for a young man deciding to take on a new land. He had been prepared to die for King and Country; now that his services were no longer required, he could take on the much slighter challenge of getting himself a proper job in advance of English soldiers finding their ways home from combat.

By any standard, he was a good prospect: six feet tall, lithe and muscular, hard-working, resourceful, and only twenty-three. He also possessed an unerring eye for detail, having scoured books on art since his teenage years, and perfect recall. Gabriel decided to present himself the next day at Christie's on King Street.

The doorkeeper, who had strict instructions to prevent soldiers from entering, attempted to bustle him away. Gabriel realized full well why he was being shooed off. Soldiers may have saved England, but they were not the kinds of persons who offered bids on precious works of art — instead they would wander in drunk from nearby pubs, look around, loiter, and in general make nuisances of themselves.

He confessed that he was looking for work, any kind of work, and was granted an interview with the head porter. Ten minutes later, Gabriel — and his tremendous powers of persuasion — had the job. He was to begin at eight the next morning.

The job was taxing, tedious, and tiring. But Gabriel looked at many pictures and eavesdropped on many conversations. He listened intently to the decrees of Anthony Blunt and Denis Mahon, keeping his eyes focused on the canvases he brought up for them to scour. Blunt was often called in to consult about Poussins, and would legislate to the experts who depended on his opinion. The erudite but short-tempered Mahon pontificated on Italian pictures. There was a style to such discourse, a certain way of convincing a listener you were totally correct about any assertion you made regarding colour, brushstroke, the quality of the canvas, a painter's signature, the lack of a painter's signature. An expert took all these factors into account within five seconds of looking at a picture. Even if you didn't know what you were talking about, you assumed an air of complete authority. Confidence purchased infinite rewards. Gabriel learned their patter, and quite soon his eye was complemented by a gift for seemingly idle but extremely precise chatter.

The experts started discussing him among themselves. Menial tasks at the great English auction houses were often performed by teenagers from families that dealt in art, an education through osmosis that was supposed to assist them at the outset of their professional lives. What was a twenty-three-year-old from Canada doing among them?

At various times, Gabriel told his colleagues that before enlisting in the Army he had had a brief stint in the art trade in Canada. At other times, he pointed out that he had been an avid reader of art books since childhood.

Within three months, no one cared why Gabriel knew so much. The simple fact was that the youngster, who bore a remarkable resemblance to Gary Cooper, had established himself as a connoisseur of the first rank.

At the time that he was made second in Old Masters, the section was investigating four Canalettos in immaculate condition. Mr. Speers, the head of the section, was to authenticate them and put them into a sale. On his fourth day, Gabriel arrived early for work and called his superior aside. He had spent the previous afternoon at the London Library, and had discovered that a bridge in one of the pictures had had considerable work done on it well after Canaletto's death — a restoration that was in the picture. Mr. Speers, thanking his lucky stars for having been sent such a virtuous apprentice, informed the vendor that he had no interest in any of the canvases.

FOR THREE YEARS, Gabriel roomed in Earl's Court with an Australian and a New Zealander, both of whom worked in the city and had decided to remain in England for a few years. In October 1949, the Australian told Gabriel about a house on Malden Road, one of the best areas in London, that was going for a song. When Gabriel said it sounded too big for one person, the Australian told him, "Buy it as an investment, mate. You're settling here. Land is your best bet."

Malden Road was, to Gabriel, the quintessential London street — the kind of setting he envisioned when reading authors like John Galsworthy. Once upon a time he had thought such a house beyond his means. Now, acting quickly and stretching his financial resources to the limit, he snapped it up. He became a Man of Property. A year later, he opened his own gallery. In relatively short order, he had reinvented himself as a Londoner.

THE METEORIC RISE of Gabriel Brown did not go unnoticed. Many of Gabriel's colleagues at Christie's kept watch on him, expecting him to stumble — a moment they would relish. When such an event did not take place, they placidly shrugged their shoulders and paid no further attention.

The truth was that Gabriel fit in more and more. In his early London days he relished everything English, to a degree that his friends and acquaintances thought verged on the macabre. How could anyone be so entranced with a soot-ridden metropolis filled with bombed-out derelict buildings? But Gabriel did not mind coke boilers, water geysers, back-to-back housing, and narrow cobbled streets. The almost universal lack of central heating was not an impediment as far as he was concerned. He coped with meat rationing, butter rationing, sugar rationing, tea rationing, egg rationing, and soap rationing. He accepted heavy coins, heavy shoes, heavy tweed coats and suits. He embraced the entire kit and caboodle of austerity Britain. Like a child visiting an enchanted toy shop, Gabriel relished red telephone boxes, trams, trolley buses, Lyons Corner houses, and the omnipresent cinemas.

In those days, he could catch glimpses of people like Augustus

John, Evelyn Waugh, and Lucien Freud eating at places like L'Étoile on Charlotte Street or Le Tour Eiffel on Rathbone Place. He spent one evening listening to Dylan Thomas declaim his verse at The Wheatsheaf in Soho. Once, at twilight, he saw an emaciated T.S. Eliot, his trouser legs rolled up, scuttling into another Soho pub, The Pillars of Hercules.

When Prince Philip of Greece married Princess Elizabeth in 1947, many were suspicious of him because some of his sisters had married German noblemen on the side of the Nazis. But Gabriel was an ardent defender of the Greek noble. As an outsider who wished to settle in England, he identified with Philip.

Gabriel mourned when George VI passed away in 1952. He purchased a television set in order to watch the new Queen's coronation in June 1953, and invited his next-door neighbours to join him. He was one of the organizers of Malden Road's street party held later in the day. When Eden invaded Egypt and seized the Suez Canal, Gabriel defended the prime minister's controversial action to everyone he knew.

E.M. Forster once claimed that if asked to choose between loyalty to country or loyalty to a friend, he would choose his friend. Gabriel insisted that this choice betrayed a colossal error in judgment. He told more than one person — then and later — that living in the United Kingdom was a huge adventure, more thrilling than any escapade he had ever embarked upon. He had never felt he belonged in Canada; in Britain, he fit in. He never became one of those Anglophiles who became more English than the English; rather, he saw in his new country an analogy for his own rebuilding. If England could be reconstructed, so could he. But he never told anyone why he needed restoration.

LONDON WAS THE logical place for someone of Gabriel's interests: the opera, ballet, theatres, and museums were reopening.
If not in droves, wealthy collectors nevertheless were returning to Christie's and Sotheby's. In 1947, there was a French
tapestries exhibition at the Victoria and Albert; shortly afterwards, a showing of art treasures from Munich and Vienna;
and then a stupendous exhibition of Dutch and Flemish
paintings at the Royal Academy.

Like everyone involved in the arts, Gabriel was aware
of the 1951 Festival of Britain as soon as preliminary plans
were formulated. The excitement was palpable. The government had found a way to announce to the world that England
had not only survived the war, but was on the verge of a
renaissance.

Some Londoners were openly skeptical. Much-needed
money for social welfare schemes was being squandered in a
futile attempt to gloss over increasingly dire living conditions.
Gabriel too may have been aware that the Festival was a bit
of public relations scam, but he embraced it wholeheartedly.
He told friends and acquaintances that he was thrilled by
the Dome of Discovery and the Lion and Unicorn Pavilion,
was moved by what the organizers claimed was the motivation behind the entire venture. He could see how England
was rising from the ashes.

"The English", he said, "are endowed with not one single
characteristic that is peculiar to themselves — nevertheless,
when taken together, they could not be mistaken for any other
nation in the world."

There is a photograph of Gabriel from 15 October 1958.
On that evening, seven paintings from the estate of Jakob

Goldschmidt, a Berlin banker who fled Nazi Germany before the war, were on the block. The sales catalogue was in full colour, a first. Closed-circuit televisions were available for those who could not squeeze into the crowded salesroom. A dress code of black ties and evening gowns was in place. The actor Kirk Douglas, the ballerina Margot Fonteyn, and the novelist Somerset Maugham were among the luminaries. The sensation of the evening was the sale of Cézanne's *Le garçon au gilet rouge* for the then-record-breaking price of £220,000, five times the price ever achieved by a work of art. Twelve long years after the end of the war, glamour had returned in full force to the English art world.

In the photograph, Gabriel stands next to Peter Wilson, a former MI5 operative and then-chairman of Sotheby's. Gabriel smiles somewhat shyly at the camera, but the glint in his eye reveals that he knows he has chosen the correct profession.

HIS LONG AFFAIR with Vivien Hampton began in 1946. He had known many women before her, but she captured his heart. When they saw the revival of *Gone with the Wind*, he told her that her green eyes had the same sparkle in them as Vivien Leigh's Scarlett.

For a few years they were inseparable. They were always together at parties and openings; once, they even attended Ascot. She took him to visit her family. Physically, theirs was an ardent relationship.

Trouble began when Gabriel mentioned that he had visited Algonquin Park in northern Ontario. Vivien found his descriptions of the landscape awe-inspiring, and she told him she would like to visit it. He looked at her as if she were mad.

She began to ask him to be open about his feelings, to share his most intimate thoughts with her. Befuddled and more than a little embarrassed, he demurred. When she insisted, he stopped telephoning. When she summoned up the courage to phone him, he was distant. When she resolved to wait, the relationship ended. There was no bitter break, no dramatic argument; the relationship simply ended. When she saw him a decade later, as she was entering Harrod's and he leaving, they pretended not to notice one another.

After his break with Vivien, Gabriel had a number of women friends, but his relationships with them never lasted more than half a year, if that. He always made his exit in anticipation of the "intimacy interrogations" he loathed.

AT THE END of 1950, Gabriel set up on Albemarle Street as a dealer. Because he had networked exceedingly well while he was at Christie's, he had more than a passing acquaintance with everyone in the art world: museum directors, curators, collectors, dealers, auction house experts. He was successful from the outset. Collectors, especially, trusted him. Many who might have consigned a major picture to auction instead invited Gabriel to sell on their behalf. Those who did not wish to appear in sales rooms at auction houses asked him to bid for them. Such commissions, especially at the outset, shored him up. Soon thereafter, he acquired and sold many important paintings by Tintoretto, Titian, Romney, Velázquez, and other artists of that calibre. In short order, he had become an important person in the rarefied art world of postwar London.

PART TWO

MISDEMEANOURS

CHAPTER TEN

To my considerable surprise, Amelia likes the sample chapter. "He's so alive in your writing. I feel he's returned from the dead." She is a very kind but completely unrealistic person.

"You like what I've written because you have a vivid memory of him and can make use of it. Most readers will not have that advantage. They're going to wonder what inner compulsions drove him, and those are absent from my pages. I don't feel he's there, no matter how hard I've tried to make him come alive. I cannot solve the jigsaw puzzle that is Gabriel Brown."

I confess my aversion to everything a biographer has to do to earn a living. Such a person may style himself a private investigator but really he is a troublemaker, a burglar snooping into the secrets of others. Brown broke with Hampton because she wanted to know too much. He would have despised me.

Amelia intervenes. "You're not doing Gabriel a disservice. He's dead now. It's alright for you to make your enquiries." When she sees the look of dismay on my face, she politely asks, "You don't believe in ghosts, do you?"

"No. I never have. But I wonder if the only dignity left to us is the secret life that we do not wish others to see. By definition, a good biographer unmasks his subject and, in the process, skewers him."

"But don't you do exactly the same in your fiction writing? You have to show the reader the inner compulsions of your characters."

"That may be so. But those people are invented. They never existed."

"I don't believe you. You can only create from what you know."

"Right. So I borrow a trait of Aunt Sybil and then affix it to one of Cousin John's. No single person's existence is being ransacked."

❧

JACOB HAS BECOME a problem child, but not in a way I ever expected. He has informed his mother that he wishes to live with Dad. He's still willing to spend every other weekend with her, but he wants to shift his principal place of residence.

I thought the expression of such a wish would drive Stella stark raving mad, but this has not happened. Instead, she is suggesting that "everything" — meaning our separation and divorce — happened too fast, and perhaps we should move slowly in making further decisions about Jacob.

I tell Jacob I am not sure his wish to re-settle with me is a good one. "A boy your age needs his mum," I blithely assure him.

I don't want to remind him of the horrible weekends he has endured in my company. There was the tragic afternoon

I took seven-year-old Jacob on the Tube to Baker Street to visit Madame Tussauds. Though he was put off by the representation of Mrs. Thatcher, he had no trouble with the spectacle of Jack the Ripper and his victims. But the piercing sounds of the Daleks — sworn enemies of Dr. Who — completely undid him. He shrieked and grabbed my hand, and we ran for the exit.

I, as a child, would have suppressed my fear. It was the way I was brought up — I was expected to be a little man. I did not share feelings with my parents.

WHY DID CANADA not exert any kind of pull for Brown? Why did he become such a Eurosnob?

Amelia tries to evade the question: "He bought and sold Old Masters."

But why the complete evasion of his past? "He never went back to Canada. Was this loathing, fear, or both?" I ask her. "I know there is a secret, but I'm not sure I wish to be the person who uncovers it."

Amelia nods her head sagely, the way she does before challenging something I have just said. "Guy, I think you are going to have to visit Canada and discover whatever you can about Gabriel's early life. You owe this basic courtesy to your subject."

CHAPTER ELEVEN

ᴥ

The act of travelling to Canada is far easier than the emotional preparation for it. You take the Piccadilly Line to Heathrow, hop off, make your way to the Air Canada booth, queue patiently for two hours for your boarding pass, and then, after another hour's wait, enter the sleek-nosed monster that will transport you to Toronto in just under eight hours.

When I announce my upcoming journey, Jacob is horrified. The new turn in our relationship means that he feels that he is being emotionally, as well as physically, left behind. "You can't leave me with Mum for three weeks!"

"Your mother will take good care of you," I assure him.

"She will not! She doesn't care about anyone but herself!"

Once upon a time, these harsh words might have been music to my ears, but, knowing as I do how easily one parent can be a scapegoat one moment and a hero the next, I am not inclined to agree to this character assassination. Having recently assumed the role of hero, I decide to be generous: "You'll be fine with Mum. I'll be back lickety-split."

AMELIA INSISTS ON making the journey to Heathrow with me, even going to the expense of hiring a car. She is visibly upset on the way. I wonder if she is leery lest I discover some unpleasant facts about Gabriel; to my surprise, however, she reveals that she is worried about me. "I imagine you'll have terrible culture shock. And I know you're going to worry needlessly about Jacob."

I assure her that I will take everything in stride. "It's only three weeks, and I decided to splurge on a really good hotel. I'll eat at McDonald's to make up for that indulgence." She laughs and tells me she doesn't want to worry about my eating junk food.

The flight — assisted by three gin and tonics — is both short and pleasant. I bestow my best Buddha grin on flight attendants and fellow passengers. Even the screaming babies do not disturb my equilibrium. Reality sets in only when the captain announces that we are about to land in Toronto.

～ُ

UNLIKE GABRIEL BROWN, Mum and Dad found postwar England stifling. "No room for advancement in Britain, we felt," Dad told me just before I set off on my trip. "We didn't have fancy manners or accents. Although we knew the streets weren't paved with gold, we thought we could get ahead in Canada."

I was not born, technically speaking, in Toronto. Upon arrival in Canada, my parents purchased a house in a subdivision in Mississauga, a sprawling urban mass that proudly served as a bedroom suburb for the metropolis. Every weekday, my father travelled into Toronto. My mother accompanied him on the way to her own job, until she was seven months pregnant with me and began to suffer from high blood pressure.

"Turns out that living is tough everywhere. We never took to Canada — it may have been Mississauga that did us in. No real centre to it. Toronto is more of a proper city. But we couldn't afford Toronto. When you were three we decided to pack it in and return to what we knew, even though we didn't like it very much."

ON THE TAXI ride from the airport into Toronto, I notice enormous spaces between buildings. I'm not sure I like this. I'm a true Brit; I like overcrowding.

My room at the InterContinental is, as promised, palatial. The fourth-floor window overlooks the Michael Lee-Chin Crystal façade of the Royal Ontario Museum, a dowdy building in the near distance transformed into glitzy shards of glass being hurled towards the viewer. I decide I'm enough of a postmodernist to like this mingling of Victorian rectitude with ritzy, in-your-face modernism. Sometimes the public must be inveigled into a museum. I like the carefully conceived serendipity of that ploy.

I stroll around the Bloor Street and Yorkville area. The shopping is very Bond Street: all the fanciest brand names — Hermès, Rolex, Chanel, Pottery Barn, Restoration Hardware — are present, but accompanied by the somewhat down-market Gap and Roots, which Stella has informed me is a famous Canadian brand name for expensive sports clothing. "Please buy clothes for Jacob there," she said. "He'll want something authentically Canadian, though most of it is made in China."

Now that the Air Canada gin has worn off, I access the sad feelings I had hoped to avoid. I return to the hotel, order room service, and put myself to bed.

End of Day One. Less than three weeks to go.

Chapter Twelve

❧

My best defence against homesickness is to hurl myself into the task of finding out as much as possible about the elusive Gabriel Brown. Web-based queries have not borne fruit, but when I telephone the archivist at the University of Toronto, a Miss Granger, I discover that she has been toiling hard on my behalf.

"Gabriel Brown graduated from University College in 1944 near the end of the War. He read Modern Languages. He had decent marks. Father was Roderick Brown; mother's given name was Rosemary. They lived in the College Park area of Toronto. He died in 2010. You know all that?"

I tell her I do.

"Well, I don't have any other official information to share with you. But I see that a colleague of mine has annotated this file. A year ago, a cousin of Brown's telephoned and asked for the same information you're seeking. She stated that our information was wrong about the death date, but didn't say how we were misinformed. I have her phone number."

CECILIA DOWBIGGEN IS not at all surprised when I ring her. "I figured someone would eventually telephone and we could get everything straightened out. Would you like to come to tea this afternoon?"

Mrs. Dowbiggen once resided in a splendid Rosedale mansion, but now lives in a condominium three blocks away from her old home, having moved when her health began to deteriorate. "A lady never reveals her age, but I am a person of advanced years. I couldn't manage any longer. Here," she sweeps her arms across the condo, "I have only three bedrooms to worry about."

The lady's years have not in any way dimmed her memory. When I ask what of the information provided by the University of Toronto is incorrect, she is ready for me.

"Well. After Gabriel went to war, no one heard from him again. His mother and father were dead and he was an only child. No one tried very hard to find him. We assumed he had been killed. The Defence Department in Ottawa was completely unhelpful. Their excuse: common surname, easily confused, etc.

"Two years ago I saw the obituary of Gabriel Brown, the London dealer, in the *Globe*, where it was mentioned that he had graduated in 1944 from University College in the University of Toronto. The person in the photograph was not my cousin."

"Gabriel may have aged differently from what you'd expected," I offer.

"You think I'm deluded?"

"Not at all, but these things happen."

"THE MAN IN the obituary photograph was a looker. Gabriel was as plain as they make them. The most exotic thing about him was his Christian name. His deluded mother chose the name Gabriel because my newborn cousin so reminded her of an angel.

"Gabriel's parents died in a car crash when he was eight. Although they lost almost everything in the crash of 1929, they were once rich. In spirit, he was an aristocrat."

"Perhaps it would help if I show you some photographs of Gabriel?"

"That might be a start."

I take the few snaps borrowed from Amelia out of my briefcase for her to inspect. She looks carefully.

"Just what I thought. Your Gabriel Brown is not my Gabriel Brown. In fact, looking at these photos, I remember this man quite clearly. Don't know why I didn't put two and two together earlier. Gabriel introduced me to him at a party. I couldn't take my eyes off him. His name was John Martin."

"Like the nineteenth-century painter John Martin?"

"Yes. Exactly. Your John Martin did not attend U of T, of that I am certain. He was some poor waif that Gabriel found on the street. My cousin had a habit of taking in strays, befriending them. If memory serves, Martin worked part time as a handyman in the music department at U of T."

Both befuddled and flabbergasted, I'm not quite sure what to ask next. "You're one hundred percent certain of this?"

"Yes. Absolutely."

"What kind of relationship did Brown and Martin have?"

"Gabriel, God bless him, was a simple kind soul who loved books. He was an orphan, and he was drawn to those who were bereft. But there was nothing to inherit from him, no possible financial gain. For the life of me, I can't think why John Martin stole his name."

I SPEND THE following morning on the phone. A John Martin had briefly been employed by the university as a piano tuner. Later, the Department of National Defence in Ottawa informs me that a serviceman named John Martin, born in 1922, had died in London late in 1945. He was never sent to a theatre of war. When I ask if the record of his passing provides any other information, I am told that John Martin was attended in the last few days of life by his good and devoted friend Gabriel Brown.

HOW AM I going to discover anything about John Martin? It's a fairly common name. The birth registry will not be of any use. The only possibility is that someone in the university's Music department might know someone who worked there in the 1940s.

On my third day in Canada, I trudge over to the Edward Johnson Building that houses the Faculty of Music. The administrative staff look at me compassionately: *Why is this lunatic Englishman asking about a long-ago part-time employee of whom we have no knowledge?*

I decide to invent the Boyd method, which is to hang around the building for a few hours and approach the oldest-looking person working there.

Rita has been a custodian in the Music department from before it moved into the Johnson building. I ask her if she is, by any chance, still in touch with anyone who worked with her thirty years ago — maybe this way I can find someone who was around in Martin's time. Rita tells me no. However, she points out Cora, whose mother had worked in the old building "donkey's years ago."

Cora was second on my shortlist before I settled on Rita. She is immediately intrigued by the strange query. "Mum's sharp as a tack, and that's the kind of thing she might remember."

The following day, I take the Tube — or the subway, as it is called in Canada — to the nursing home on the Danforth where Cora's mother Myrtle now resides. The Danforth reminds me of the Portobello Market, except pedestrians are not blocked by vendors hawking their wares. The nursing home, close to the street, is brightly lit, welcoming in what I consider the Canadian way. The space is efficiently arranged, but still maintains a homespun atmosphere.

Myrtle, equipped with a walker and dressed in what North Americans call a housecoat, is waiting for me in the foyer. Short of stamina but precise of mind, the old lady invites me to her room. "Close the door," she commands politely. "The walls have ears here. My companions have the impression that we share everything."

Cora has told her mother why I wished to see her. I am certain that her John Martin must be my Gabriel Brown, and when I show her snapshots from the 1940s she nods.

"That's him. Must have been nineteen or twenty when I knew him. I passed the time of day with him quite often. Big strapping lad. Always pleasant. Hard worker. He was a gregarious fellow. He had eyes for the ladies, and they returned the compliment. He could have parked his shoes under my bed any time. Everyone liked him. He hung around with students in the evening. His friends were those interested in art and, of course, music. I never knew much about him. I once heard he was on the lam, but I was never told why he was in trouble. I have no idea what happened to him. I'm not surprised he joined the Army."

"Did Martin have any close friends besides Gabriel Brown?"

"Haven't thought about this since back then, but there was that strange woman. Her name was Hedy Myers. She was a student in the Fine Arts department, but she was always hanging out at the Music school. Older than her friends, maybe in her mid-twenties. She never spoke to the likes of me, but I saw her in action many times. I always wondered why John was so nice to her. She had a high opinion of herself and a nasty streak to boot. I don't envy you having to ask that creature for help, if she's still breathing."

CHAPTER THIRTEEN

W hite on white on white. This is an accurate description of both Hedy Myers and her flat. The walls are snow coloured, as are her curtains, upholstered chair and sofa, plastic chairs, and walls. She coyly informs me it is to match her hair: "It turned completely white when I was thirty. When I read how Syrie Maugham had pioneered all-white rooms in the Twenties, I was hooked."

Myers has a refined, sleek face and a body to complement it. She is dressed in matching cream blouse and trousers. The cream is the only relief from white in the entire flat. Perhaps I'm still suffering from jet lag, but my equilibrium, perilous at the best of times, has been completely upended. I find it difficult to distinguish the lady from her furnishings, and have the uneasy feeling that I am speaking to a ghost.

Miss Myers — as she instructs me to address her — lives on the fifth floor of the Colonnade on Bloor Street. The view outside her window is one of boisterous city life: well-heeled shoppers on the march, posh cars moving self-importantly along.

I am ensconced in a bourgeois bower of bliss.

"I knew John Martin briefly in the Forties. We were lovers for about a year, on and off. We quarreled a great deal. We weren't exactly a good match. John was a smooth operator, but underneath the façade he had the soul of a country bumpkin."

"You mean he wasn't a sophisticated person?"

"I guess you could put it that way. He was too much of an idealist for me."

"An idealist?"

"He was a communist. Believed in the proletariat. Art for the people. I've never wanted to carry that baggage."

"What do you know about his early life? Did he discuss it with you?"

"Never. I heard tell that he was born in Toronto, in that slummy part called the Ward, ran away at an early age, went up north briefly, and then returned to the city. He never talked about such things. I never asked, mind you." Suddenly — probably because she wants to be rid of me — the lady changes tack. "I know a deep dark secret about John Martin." Seeing my ears perk up, she continues. "I'm not going to incriminate myself. I'll allow my ex-husband do so. After John Martin, I married Herbert Bland. Do you know who he is?"

"He's a dealer. Somewhere close to here. On Avenue Road?"

"You've done your homework, sonny!" Without any attempt to hide the smirk that now decorates her face, she continues: "Make an appointment with him. Tell him on my behalf that he is to tell you the Martin secret. He won't want it revealed. Could do him enormous harm professionally." Her smirk becomes a sneer. "I think what he will disclose will be of enormous assistance in your biographical labours."

AT FIRST, HERBERT Bland sounds like he might live up to his surname. On the phone he is polite, even courtly. Only when I ask for an appointment do I hear the hard edge in his voice: "I can't clear my calendar before next week," he primly announces.

I resolve to spend some time at the Art Gallery of Ontario and make myself aware of Canadian art. The concierge at the hotel tells me that if I am "open" to the ROM, I will "fall in love" with Frank Gehry's reinvention of the AGO. In the main, he is right. The blue titanium roof reaching for the sky momentarily takes my breath away. *Large Two Forms*, the Henry Moore sitting outside the building, reminds me why I have always responded to his monumental and inviting sculptures. The enormous plaster casts in the Moore Sculpture Centre make me feel like I am walking on the moon with phantoms.

Before I set off for Canada, both my parents instructed me to look carefully at anything I could see by the Group of Seven. "They were all the rage when we were in Canada. In the process of being rediscovered. We really liked them. Bright, vivid colours. Those men saw landscape in a whole new way. Completely original. Nothing like them in English art."

For once, my sometimes philistine progenitors have gotten it right. The Canadian art is, for me, a revelation. The robust reds used by Varley, MacDonald, and Jackson are ingratiating, and I immediately bond with Tom Thomson, the man who inspired the Seven well before they were a Group. James Morrice's Caribbean canvases. What amazing, pure sensuality! The Krieghoffs are a pleasant surprise. He must have been a merry old bloke. The people in the pictures are having a ripping good time.

The concierge at the InterContinental — he read Art History at U of T — assured me that Lawren Harris was the best of the lot. The Lake Superior and Arctic images are too blue and thus too cold for my liking. I do like his city views of Toronto — including his paintings of the Ward, the area Hedy Myers claims John Martin was raised in. Harris's canvases give me a vivid sense of the place: it was obviously a centre of poverty, malnutrition, and brutality. Happily, it no longer exists.

~

THERE ISN'T ANYONE else to interview until my meeting with Bland, so I decide to visit the City of Toronto Archives to learn more about the Ward.

It was an area in central Toronto bounded by today's College Street, Queen Street, Yonge Street, and University Avenue, centered on the intersection of Bay and Albert Streets. From the late nineteenth century until the Twenties, the Ward was the home of refugees from the European revolutions of 1848 and the Irish Potato Famine, as well as those who escaped via the Underground Railroad. Also living there were many impoverished Jews and, a bit later, the Chinese who arrived in Canada to work on the railway. One hundred thousand people — including many of Toronto's outcasts — were squeezed into that small space.

One commentator from 1915 was outspoken about the miserable existences eked out there: "In rough-cast houses, plaster has fallen off, and there is, more or less, an absence of paint or whitewash. Fences about the houses have partly collapsed and no effort is made to repair them or to remove them altogether. Sidewalks leading to the houses and doorsteps are in a broken condition, and the doors them-selves are usually in a state of ill repair. Wooden shutters sag from one hinge or have many slats missing. Rags and unused clothing lie scattered about, mingled with broken pieces of furniture, tin cans, broken stovepipe, and other junk, without any danger of being disturbed by the residents." It was such a strange and fearful place that no respectable citizen would wander there in daylight, and "after dark — no sane person would dream of running such a risk! The danger that lurks in these crowded streets is not always clearly formulated in the minds of those who fear it; perhaps it is the dagger of an Italian desperado of which they dream — perhaps the bearded faces of the 'Sheenies' are sufficient in themselves to inspire terror — but at any rate the fear remains and probably it could best be analyzed as Fear of the Unknown."

I decide to look at the Archives' photographs. The men and women who wandered the Ward, cameras at the ready, wanted to show the inhumane conditions in which these members of the underclass existed. As I expect, the photos are much starker than any Lawren Harris painting: the buildings are often reduced to rubble; there are huge areas of land on which sit only broken bricks and dog turds; the residents usually avert their glances from the camera, their eyes full of shame.

I should know that life can undo any semblance of good-ness and decency, but as I go photograph by dreary photograph through the archival boxes, the feeling overwhelms me. I am not on the verge of tears. No, the feeling is more one of nausea at the ways in which men so readily construct prisons for other men. John Martin might have wished to purge all memory of living in such wretched conditions.

Then one picture takes my breath away. A boy, about Jacob's age, stands among rubble. He stands up straight, his shoulders drawn back, his hands on his hips. He has placed his right foot on top of a large piece of rock. He looks defiantly at the person who is taking his snapshot. There is not a hint of a smile.

It takes me a few moments to realize I am staring into the eyes of John Martin.

IT TAKES ME two days at the central birth registry to find that my John Martin was born on January 12, 1922 to Joseph and Evelyn Martin, whose residence was 47 Terauley Street. Terauley is now Bay Street, and number 47 is now subsumed by a skyscraper constructed in 1995; any sentimental thoughts of visiting my subject's birthplace vanish.

Chapter Fourteen

※⌒

I am less than enthusiastic about my birthplace, to the relief
of Mum and Dad. I am providing further evidence, if any is
needed, that their decision many years ago to return to base
was sound. They are similarly unstinting about my words
of praise for the Group. "I too have a soft spot for Varley," my
father assures me.

There are many awkward pauses in my phone calls to Jacob.
"I love our new place," he says over and over again, poignantly
reminding me that he has become attached to Gabriel Brown's
home. If he misses me, he isn't going to fess up. I am crushed.

Like Jacob, Amelia is not a great communicator on the
phone. "These overseas trunk calls must be costing you a
fortune." Fearing the expense — probably a habit of mind
acquired during what she calls the Hitler War — she says little.
For my part, I am deliberately withholding; I have resolved
not to tell her about John Martin until we see each other.

I remain homesick, mostly for Jacob. I also find it increasingly difficult to know what I think about Toronto. When I

compare it to London, it gets the short end of the stick on all counts. Toronto has one magnificent street, University Avenue; a desultory portion of Yonge Street that is said incorrectly to resemble Soho; and a sport stadium, the Rogers Centre, that is like being inside an ocean liner. In contrast, London is an assortment of villages linked by the grim but friendly Underground: worldly North London areas like Camden Town; sedate, expensive South Kensington; and the concert halls and other cultural hubs on the South Bank. There is also the Thames, along which all manner of ornate buildings have been erected.

I am an impartial, untrustworthy tourist because I am a creature who does not like to wander far from his nest; I am being unfair to Toronto because it is not London. Like John Martin, I would have traded the New World for the Old.

～

THE ENGLISH ARE said to have cornered the market in seediness. Herbert Bland and his gallery call the accuracy of this claim into question.

The shops on his stretch of Avenue Road are what we sometimes condescendingly call *bijoux*: small tony boutiques in which unusual pieces of jewelry are on offer, expensive clothes from every part of the world are on sale, and "country-style" antiques are priced soaringly high.

"Bland Fine Arts" is an outcast among its neighbours. The display areas on either side of the door are bereft of anything other than junk: Coke bottles, Pepsi cans, dust bunnies, and other debris. The electricity is defunct, and the walls are bare.

At first I am not sure that the proprietor has remembered our appointment, but then I notice that the door is ajar.

Timidly, I walk in and call hello. A shuffling sound emanates from the back, and a short, aged man emerges gradually
from the darkness.

"Welcome to my rag and bone shop," he greets me.

Mr. Bland looks like an angry walrus. His tiny eyes and
wide forehead are placed atop the largest set of jowls I have
ever beheld. There are no chairs on hand, so we stand in the
entrance as he looks me up and down with a hint of contempt.

"Hedy has unleashed you on me," he begins.

I apologize for inconveniencing him and mutter something about having been commissioned to write a life of
Gabriel Brown.

"You now know that identity is a fabrication. His name
was John Martin. The same as the famous painter."

"So I gather." I want to do everything in my power to keep
this conversation under my control. I revert to the role of
the timid, earnest researcher.

"My ex-wife has informed me that she will menace me
unless I make you aware of what she calls 'the big secret.'"

I nod.

"John Martin was a denizen of the underclass when I met
him in 1942. In those days I was a student in Fine Art at U of T.
I had an inheritance to spend and was thinking about setting
up as a dealer when I completed university. John had just
turned twenty and was working at the Faculty of Music. He
was Hedy's sweetheart, if such a word can be used to describe
anyone who makes the mistake of becoming involved with
her.

"John and I became pals. We talked about art all the time.
He had a ready eye and a steady hand when he put pencil to

paper, and spent all his spare time drawing and painting. He did this while working as an odd-job man. I suspect he stole the paper and paints.

"In the kind of way that young people joke and carry on, I challenged him to replicate the work of some well-known painter. Although he claimed he could easily win such a contest, he didn't like the idea at all. The idea of making a false Tom Thomson particularly appalled him. 'Well, what about someone of an earlier generation,' I asked. 'What about Cornelius Krieghoff?'

"Even in those days the market was flooded with canvases by the Amsterdam-born painter. He's quite easy to copy. You just show a bunch of people happily partying.

"John was adamant such an act was a complete desecration. He changed his mind only when Hedy made it clear that she would withdraw her sexual favours unless he accepted the test. That's how it all began."

"What do you mean by 'it all'?" I ask.

"The Krieghoff forgeries. The first one was superb. Impossible to distinguish from a real one. His resolve was weakened, and he allowed me to market the picture. I quickly sold it to some Bay Street magnate. John made many more and a system was established. He made the paintings. I marketed them and provided all the supplies. We split the profits. The whole process was as easy as winking.

"We carried on for two highly profitable years. Suspicions were aroused when so many Krieghoffs became available so quickly. The police began to investigate, and John became a hunted man. Very soon after that, he vanished. I later learned that he had enlisted with his friend, Gabriel Brown.

"I subsequently became a respectable dealer, married Hedy, eventually had all my resources ransacked by her, and here I am."

"Did you know Martin had become a dealer in London?"

"Of course, his photograph appeared in the journals all the time. I realized that my old pal had done very well for himself, and decided to allow sleeping dogs to remain snoring. We wouldn't be having this conversation today unless Hedy was intent on aggravating me."

"Why do you think he changed his name?"

Bland's entire manner changes. The contempt vanishes and I am left with a sad old man recalling the past. There are a few tears on display on his wizened face. With nothing to fear from the police thanks to the statute of limitations, he — in his own perverse way — seems to appreciate being forced into making a half-hearted confession. "I have often thought about that. He must have wanted to evade the authorities. Or he might have wanted to have a new beginning."

~

FOR THE FIRST time, I begin — somewhat against my will — to empathize with Martin/Brown. So he was, like myself, a would-be artist. Nothing wrong there. Was a person who manufactured fakes really an evil person? What harm was being done?

I know many of the masterpieces of Western art were made to please wealthy collectors anxious to aggrandize themselves. When all is said and done, isn't collecting merely a childish rivalry among a bunch of well-heeled rich men? So what if they get stung from time to time? I wasn't going to get too upset about that. For me, plagiarism has never been a huge issue. I take the good-enough-for-Shakespeare approach, and the Krieghoff knockoffs sound like a boyhood prank gone too far. Gabriel had a devil-may-care side to him. As far as I am concerned, that is another point in his favour.

CHAPTER FIFTEEN

❧

Only five more days in Canada. I am holing up in my hotel room to write the opening chapter of the biography. This way I will have something to show Amelia when I get back.

I have only fragments to work with, being almost completely dependent upon Bland, an embittered old man whose memory may be faulty. I also suspect him of being mendacious. When I asked him about his friend's childhood, Bland recalled bits and pieces of reminiscences confided to him by John Martin. I have tried to arrange them in chronological order, but I am building a house of cards on shifting sands, making unfounded assumption after unfounded assumption. There is a lot more romanticized conjecturing than painstaking biographical reconstruction in my new chapter.

Gabriel Brown (1922–1945)
HE IS FALLING, ever so gently. Then he awakes. Another time, he is falling towards the ground much faster — it will be the

end of him. Then he wakes covered in sweat.

The room is always the same. The pale pink wallpaper near his head has been erased by all the heads that have rubbed against it. The only real piece of furniture, a small dresser opposite, balances itself precariously on its three remaining feet. The air in the room is sticky. The room does not have a window and thus no view of the outside.

He sleeps on a mattress in the middle, his brothers on one side, his sisters on the other. He is the baby. Dolly and Maisie look after him, often protecting him from the rough-housing of Tom and Ben.

His mother, Evelyn, is smiling. She inspects him, likes what she sees, picks him up and hands him to his father, Joe, who grasps him tightly, squeezes him, kisses him, and tells him to run off and play. His father smells sour; his mother emanates the odour of lilies of the valley.

Mother and son walk in a glade surrounded by tulips and daffodils. The sun shines.

THEIR HOME IS a lean-to assortment of small rooms attached to the side of a house. The interior of their home is dark and cramped. It is stiflingly hot in summer, bitterly cold in winter. A thick pall of dust hangs in every room; cobwebs haunt the corner walls.

John prefers to play in the street, often by himself, but he has to be careful not to get in the way of the ruffians, the boys who run around in packs. He explores more of his neigh-bourhood. The houses are falling apart. There is debris everywhere. Broken windows are left as is. Abandoned hovels are filled with cats and their waste. An ungainly assortment of tiny frame cottages, lean-tos, open drains, pit privies, junk wagons. The smells of manure and rotting plaster mingle. Tailor shops in every street. Factories of every size and description. The hawkers on the street are often jovial, but the greengrocers ruthlessly protect themselves from would-be pilferers, especially children. There are many brothels and public houses.

JOHN'S FATHER LOST his job at the garment sweatshop months ago. No one will hire him to perform even the most menial of tasks. His drinking has gotten worse. He worked briefly peddling door-to-door, but used the proceeds at his favourite pub. There is seldom any money for food.

John's parents fight all the time. Like his older brothers and sisters, he has learned to keep out of their way during the brawls.

Mother does some sewing. She often sends John out to buy potatoes. "Make sure your father does not catch sight of you. If he does, he'll steal the money and we won't have anything to eat."

John has become expert at evading his father. If he sees Joe approaching, he darts into an alleyway until he passes. No one likes Joe, not even his drinking companions. He is a man with a cruel streak.

John knows by heart his mother's many laments. She should have taken her brother's advice and not stepped out with Joe. She should never have allowed her soft feelings to get the better of her. She should not have married below her.

Evelyn tells John that she loves her children, but that they — including him — are all an awful burden.

A BEAUTIFUL SMILE. Sensitive eyes. A handsome face. John knows these compliments well. He has heard them since he was five years old, perhaps earlier. He does not practise his smile; it comes effortlessly when he is distracted, confused, even angry. It is how he deals with the world.

The neighbours compliment John's mother on how well her youngest child speaks. They can hear honey in his voice. "He'll make something of himself," they assure her.

In school he is top of his class. His printing and cursive are elegant, his teachers say. He has an excellent memory.

BY THE AGE of twelve, John has become moody. He cultivates rebellious thoughts. He loves his mother, but is repulsed by her constant exhortation that he not attempt to advance above his appointed station. He does not remind her that, in running away with his father, she deliberately stepped below hers. His father remains a sorry excuse for a human being: snarling, unkempt, and mean-spirited.

Poverty ennobles no one, John realizes, but he is aware that nature allows some to triumph over adversity. For example, the Jews in the Ward may be battered, but they maintain an even-spirited resistance. He suspects this is because they retain a strong sense of community. The same is true, in various degrees, of the other immigrant groups. He observes, however, that Anglo-Saxons allow themselves to be crushed. He resolves that this will never happen to him.

John has become adept at skipping school and wandering beyond the confines of the Ward. Sir Henry Pellatt's Casa Loma, on Walmer Road, impresses him on first viewing; but upon inspecting it a second time its turrets, enormous vegetable garden, and deer park strike him as overdone. He often peers into the Eaton's windows, but the elaborate toys are not made for someone of his class. He is attracted to the smart clothes on offer to lads of his age who attend Upper Canada College and University of Toronto Schools. Their navy blue blazers and red, white, and blue ties appeal to his acquisitive side. Some day, he promises himself, you will be smartly dressed.

JOHN IS FIFTEEN. His older siblings have not been home for two years. Both the girls are live-in maids, one at a cousin of Lady Eaton's. His two brothers have, he has been told, headed west. For a while, he was the only one left behind. Then Andrew comes along. The little baby with the blonde curly hair is fetchingly beautiful. He looks like one of Leonardo's most beguiling cherubim. John looks after him, changes his diapers, cuddles him, makes sure he has a bottle when going off to sleep.

Their father still occasionally shows up. Because John is now too tall for Joe to strike, and because Joe loves babies, John's mother bears the brunt of his rage. He hurls words of abuse at his wife before hitting her.

John is torn. He can remain at home, continue at school, and look after Andrew. That's what he feels he should do. But if he runs away, he can find work at a shop or factory that will provide him with room and board. He won't need much of his wages and, in this way, he can provide for his mother and Andrew.

John leaves. For the next three years he works in an assortment of mills. He never has a proper job: he moves heavy equipment, he sweeps floors, he cleans lavatories. Every two weeks or so he returns home with groceries and a small toy for Andrew. He gives most of his money to his mother.

Andrew is growing up quickly. He is frail and very short of stature for his age, but he has a very good natural eye. The few drawings Gabriel sees by his sibling reveal a sure, inventive hand.

"He takes after you," his mother tells him.

FOUR-YEAR-OLD Andrew is badly bruised. His tiny body carries an assortment of black and blue marks. One night, John waits for his father outside the pub. He is forthright: if Joe hits the boy again, he will answer to John. His father's bright red face is aglow with rage. He curses his son, but John knows that the older man fears him.

SCHOOL SEEMS so long ago. John had always enjoyed art lessons. Recently, he has taken to drawing. He is amazed: he can gaze at any person or house or piece of landscape and then reproduce what he sees precisely and accurately. The seventeen-year-old asks himself, *Is this what they call a God-given talent?* What an amazing power! He cannot believe his good luck.

The word "artist" starts to acquire a new meaning for him. He has heard of Michelangelo and Rubens, but he now begins to wonder what kind of artists exist in Canada. Are there any? He scours gallery windows. He feels too poorly dressed to wander inside, and doesn't fancy being shooed away. John goes to the public library and flips through slews of books.

He realizes, painfully, that most artists in Canada live like himself: hand to mouth. The exception to this rule is Lawren Harris. John reads as much as he can about the now-disbanded Group of Seven. He is amazed by their bright colours, and the almost surreal ways in which they evade reality in order to render landscape.

Most of all, he is taken with that strange untaught wild man Tom Thomson, who wandered Algonquin Park and squeezed everything he could out of the experience. Those magnificent colours, those wonderful lines, that sheer inventiveness, that overpowering breadth of imagination. Even if he had not been murdered, Thomson could never have lived long, John tells himself. Such gifts are only on loan for short periods of time. How could such a person have ever become an old man?

John travels to Algonquin Park for two-week stays. He retraces Thomson's footsteps in order to take in exactly what the artist beheld. He draws and makes a few oil sketches. At the end of his last visit, he is distraught: there is no magic in his hand. He can render what he sees, but he does not possess the gift of vision, what is sometimes called a "third eye." John can replicate; he cannot imagine.

FINALLY, AFTER FOUR STAYS in Muskoka, John returns to Toronto, a very unhappy young man with his tail very much between his legs. He abandons his factory job for one in the Faculty of Music building at the University of Toronto, where he moves pianos from building to building.

He meets Hedy and has an affair with her. He has had many women before, but those relationships had lasted at most a few days. He and Hedy, however, are together for almost ten months. She is extremely beautiful, but very brittle; he is extremely handsome and, in his own way, extremely fragile as well. She wants to know the secrets of his heart. He tells her he has secrets but shares them with no one, not even if he happens to be in love. They stop seeing each other.

Through Hedy he meets Herbert Bland, a self-proclaimed opportunist. He is the first person with whom John can discuss art. Bland has an excellent eye and is eager to be part of the art world. John confides in his new friend one of the secrets withheld from Hedy: he desperately wanted to be an artist but discovered he lacked the *sine qua non*, the link between inspiration and imitation.

"Don't let that get in your way," Herbert advises. John is puzzled.

The plan to make fake Krieghoffs is Herbert's. "Quite simple to do for someone of your abilities, old boy. Jolly farm houses, plenty of snow, drunken revelries." It's not quite as easy as Herbert lets on, but soon the two men have established a partnership. Money trickles in at first, and then there is a deluge. Many newly rich Canadians want a Krieghoff.

The two men prosper until word leaks out about the conspiracy to flood the market with Krieghoffs. The police are on the lookout for John Martin. Somehow or other, Herbert Bland's name is not mentioned.

AND SO THERE is the *hegira*, as Bland facetiously calls his friend's flight of 1944. John does not confront Bland, although he is fairly certain he has been betrayed by him.

At about the time he met Hedy and Herbert, John had

befriended the reclusive Gabriel Brown. Possessed of a magnificent name, but self-effacing in manner and puny in body, Gabriel was touched by John's interest in him. John had not feigned friendship: he enjoyed Gabriel's company and learned a great deal from the orphaned aristocrat about the ways of fashionable society.

No one would have claimed that Brown was a man of the world, but he was born of the world that fascinated John Martin. From Gabriel, he has learned to modulate his voice and give anyone with whom he converses the impression that he or she is the centre of the universe. He has begun to conduct himself like an aristocrat.

Now they both enlist. In training camp, John assists his ungainly friend. He watches over him as he once did Andrew. When they arrive in England, the war is just about over. Gabriel becomes extremely ill. The doctors can do nothing to save him. John nurses Gabriel until he dies.

John likes what he sees in England. Though he regrets that he can no longer care for his brother Andrew, he decides to stay in a place where he is not a wanted man. He substitutes his dog tag for Gabriel's, and renders John Martin a dead man. Gabriel Brown is dead, long live Gabriel Brown.

PART THREE

CRIMES

CHAPTER SIXTEEN

The flight home is six hours. My patience will not be taxed. I assure myself it is a piece of cake. In-flight movies, a short snooze, reunion with Jacob. This is about as good as it gets.

Two hours in, after the meal service has been completed and I have downed two gin and tonics, I close my eyes and anticipate two or three hours of blissful sleep. Instead, the piercing, anguished eyes of young John Martin appear before me. Other sets of eyes follow, all very similar. Where do I know these people from? Slowly, faces from each of the six portraits in Brown's exhibition catalogue emerge. The images move as if on an old-fashioned Kodak Carousel, more and more quickly, until they merge into one another.

I struggle to descend deeper into my dream, but then the plane hits an air pocket and I am wide awake, my forehead drenched in sweat. In that horrible moment, an epiphany occurs: the eyes in the six portraits and the eyes in the photograph at the City of Toronto Archive are the same. They are the eyes of John Martin.

The truth has been staring at me all along, and I have been unable to see it. He was the creator of the six canvases.

Now I see what incredible hubris the man possessed. First, he had faked and sold six masterworks. Then, he had the gall to borrow them back from the Japanese collector and the five institutions he had duped. He even assembled colour reproductions of them — and their same pairs of eyes — in a pamphlet.

Yet no one had possessed the astuteness to see it. In part, this must have been because of the magnitude of the duplicity: it was so unimaginable it went undetected. I have the advantage of having uncovered the photograph.

What made him resume his career as a forger in England? How exactly am I going to unmask Gabriel Brown? These are the questions I need to answer. And there are more delicate issues: For instance, what am I going to tell Amelia?

I had begun to form a bond of sympathy, however tenuous, with Brown. I had thought the Krieghoff forgeries youthful misdemeanours, but now I see that they were training for a brilliant criminal career. I detest him. Rather than simply uncovering the truth about his past, I want to expose him. His crimes should be known to the world.

Only a few hours to gather myself before my plane sets down at Heathrow. I will assume a convincing camouflage for Amelia. I will remain the dutiful biographer to her, while privately I assume the role of avenger. This will be my new, unsought part in this astounding scenario.

I have heard tell that many biographers come to despise their subjects because they loathe the close contact with another being more important than they. But I have uncovered a monster, pure and simple. Though I did not create the fiend as Dr. Frankenstein did his, I detest him with the same intensity.

CHAPTER SEVENTEEN

❧

As I had anticipated, Amelia is at Heathrow to welcome me. Jacob is with her, his mother having readily agreed to Amelia's plan to surprise me.

I am delighted and relieved to see them, but my discovery of Gabriel Brown's duplicity puts a damper on my spirits. I do my best to set aside my low feelings, and manage a convincing job of playacting. The three of us are in high spirits all the way to Belsize Park.

Upon arriving at the door of Brown's home, I am overcome by waves of sorrow, rather than the anger I had expected. Here again is the house divided into two parts. Have I even begun to comprehend how Brown had compartmentalized his existence?

Not a single piece of Lego clogs the floor of the sitting room. Instead, a huge sheet covers the sculpture, which has grown even larger in my absence. Jacob beams. Amelia nods at him.

"It's about time," he proudly announces, "that you see our

masterpiece. Ralph couldn't be here today, but he's given me permission to go ahead. Without further ado, here it is!"

With that, he pulls the sheet away to reveal a beautifully constructed model of a man's head. The rendition is extremely Cubist, very reminiscent of Picasso. Bright Lego yellows, reds, and blues dominate the countenance, although there has been judicious use of greens, blacks, and whites.

The portrait may be modernist, but there can be no doubt that the boys have used photographs of an older Gabriel Brown as their model. The firm jaw, the candid smile, and the benign eyes are all unmistakably his.

Although taken aback by the technical adroitness of the two lads, I feel deflated. I am looking into the face of the man who has become my enemy.

Jacob is not quite sure what emotion my face is registering. "I hope you like it. We worked hard. We decided to do Mr. Brown because he has become our patron, hasn't he? We're his guests after all."

"I love it," I assure him.

Amelia beams. "I didn't suggest the subject to the boys. I want you to know that. I must say I was thrilled when Jacob confided in me. "

I fix a steady smile on my face, then wait about an hour before I announce that I feel overwhelmed by jet lag.

∼

DEVISING A COHERENT strategy of subterfuge is difficult when suffering from fatigue. All night I toss and turn. How am I going to debunk Brown? If I announce my discovery, I will be seen as an ungrateful imbecile who could not appreciate the bounty bestowed upon him. Amelia would stare incredulously. Jacob might not believe me. Stella would say that I have found yet another way to shoot myself in the foot.

In the instance of these forgeries, I need proof beyond my own eye. The best approach, I decide, would be to take my biographical investigation in a new direction. What artists had Brown been friendly with? Could any of them shed light on his abilities as a painter? Might I learn something of Brown's ambitions as an artist? Would such a path lead me in the direction of Gabriel Brown, the forger?

CHAPTER EIGHTEEN

I tell Amelia I am not certain where I should head next in my search for information, but before she can make a suggestion I interject: "I think it would be helpful if I were to speak with any artist friends he had; that might give me the kind of insight I'm lacking at the moment. Did Gabriel form friendships with many contemporary artists?"

"Only a few, those who are collectors. In the early days of the gallery, Miss Dickinson told me that Anthony Erindale had purchased a few drawings, and the two men saw each other once or twice a year. Drinks at White's. That sort of thing."

Amelia warns me that Erindale has a high opinion of himself. "He's unfailingly polite, a real gentleman, but he makes certain that he remains the centre of any conversation. You'll have to allow for that when you interview him."

THE MUCH HONOURED and much married Erindale lives in solitary splendour in a palazzo of his own design in Chelsea. The beautiful, chaste lines of the interior deliberately — and perversely, in my opinion — clash with the installations housed inside: eternally youthful puppies floating in formaldehyde in a huge tank in one room; a twenty-times-life-size head of a horse floating in another. The viewer is supposed to be shocked into submission when he realizes he can make no sense of what he beholds.

A servant — I guess such a person would once have been called a butler — escorts me into the presence of his master. Erindale is famous as a showman, and though over ninety and slightly bent over by age, he certainly possesses a mischievous twinkle in his eye.

Erindale points at a chair near his own. Before I can ask him a question, he tells me that he is sure I have "prepped" myself to see him and, although we are to speak about Gabriel Brown, he will nevertheless tell me something about himself. The disquisition lasts about half an hour, as he regales me with scurrilous anecdotes that have never made their way into print. If I were writing his biography, I could not be more pleased.

Only when he has finished does he reflect on Brown: "He was never the most forthcoming of persons. 'Very private' is the adjective often affixed to such people. I do remember one curious episode, however."

I can tell he has fully rehearsed what he is about to say. So much for spontaneity.

"We were lunching at my club. Brown had just returned from India. He had been in Bombay — I think we're supposed to call it Mumbai these days — at some sort of conference. He told me his room had occupied a lower floor, and the lights from the hotel were bright. One evening, at twilight, he had looked down and been confronted with the dismal sight of slum dwellers crowded into shabby, rat-infested shacks. He could see the dirt caked on the faces of those people, even the holes in the rags they wore. Water buffalo were everywhere. Children being disobedient, ignoring the commands of their parents. Next-door neighbours hurling invectives at one another. A few solitary men simply sitting there, staring straight ahead. He felt plunged into hell.

"Brown said to me, 'I wish I had the talent to put that scene on canvas, but I have no aptitude for depicting the human condition.' It was a strange thing for him to say.

"Now that I'm thinking about it, there was another incident from the end of that same trip to India. He was in a taxi on the way to the airport, half asleep. When the car stopped at a light, the usual assortment of beggars descended upon it, tapping on his window. He paid no attention until, suddenly, there appeared before him a teenage boy holding a much younger child, apparently his brother, on his shoulders. The young boy smiled, as if delighted to make eye contact. But when Brown looked into the eyes of the other, he saw a young man defeated by life. Those dark brown eyes, devoid of hope, moved him. He told me that he could not eradicate the image of the two. 'I'll be haunted by them until I die.'"

I change the subject. "Do you think Brown painted?"

"I doubt it. If he did, he never told me. "

Erindale has not put paint to canvas in years — he has "gone conceptual," as he put it to me — so it is unlikely that Brown would have confided in him on this topic. In any case, the celebrated artist takes little notice of others.

MY HUNCH ABOUT interviewing artist-friends of Brown's will, I realize, lead me nowhere. Brown was a master of duplicity. He would have deliberately concealed his remarkable artistic abilities, because hiding his talent in the ground would have kept him out of harm's way.

Chapter Nineteen

In my teenage communist phase, I was riveted by John Berger's *Ways of Seeing*, a BBC series. Berger taught me that most successful artists, in order to survive, cater to wealthy patrons. The rich control the means of production lock, stock, and barrel: if someone of enormous wealth wants a certain kind of picture — one, for example, one depicting himself with his family, or himself alone, or himself with a prize horse or pig — that is what is delivered. Art has always been the eager bedroom companion of money.

I am the kind of person who likes to ignore such realities and, instead, simply look at wonderful objects and be amazed by their beauty. But with Gabriel Brown in my life, I can no longer wear a blindfold.

Brown was a man who made his money buying and then trading works of art. His patrons were the collectors, that sector of the wealthy who do not make art but wish to be surrounded by it. He pandered to such clients. But at some point, Brown decided that he no longer wanted to simply *sell* great works of art. Perhaps his ego became inflated. Perhaps his deprived early origins made him angry at or envious of his clients. In any event, while playing the part of the dutiful, slightly sycophantic dealer who unearthed wondrous treasures, he tricked those he supposedly served, chuckling to himself as he passed off one of his Murillos or Rembrandts as the real thing.

CHAPTER TWENTY

鸡

In order to unravel this charming monster's duplicities, I will have to understand the world of fakers and their frauds, one of the most intriguing areas of art history. I decide to devote a month to this pursuit at the London Library.

I tell Amelia that I consider my knowledge of the history of Western art so scant that I must steep myself in it by reading everything I can get my hands on. "I'll be better taking the Tube down to Piccadilly and working there. Art books are so heavy that they are difficult to cart back and forth."

OCCASIONALLY ENTHRALLING BUT always shabby: this is the world of the forger I now encounter daily, the world of petty criminals. Not petty in the usual sense, as when affixed to thieves; no, these men thought they could rip the souls out of the corpses of long-dead geniuses.

Among the most fascinating of these criminals is the Manhattan dealer Ely Sakhai. For twenty years, this contemporary of Brown's scoured the auction houses for genuine second- or third-rate works by the likes of Cézanne, Renoir, Chagall, Gauguin, and Klee. Some collectors who want to have a genuine Renoir do not mind if it happens to be a boring, uninteresting painting. In the fine art world, big name acquisition is sometimes a specialty, almost like collecting autographs for a scrapbook. "I have enough money to own a Renoir," is the entire point of the exercise.

Sakhai would purchase, as cheaply as possible, a canvas well beneath the qualities associated with the famous artist who painted it, and immediately send it out to be replicated by a forger. After waiting perhaps six months or a year, he would offer the duplicate to a collector with a great deal of money and little taste. Then, after a decade passed, he would consign the original to auction.

Sakhai's double-your-money scheme was brilliant, but far from foolproof. In 2000, he made the mistake of consigning the original of Gauguin's *Vase de Fleurs* to Sotheby's. He was blissfully unaware that the fake, after being passed from collector to collector, was up for auction a few miles away at Christie's. It did not take long for collectors attending the pre-sale viewing at one house to notice its twin on display at the other.

Another paltry soul was Hans van Meegeren, the Vermeer forger. Although he was a talented enough artist in his own right, he was greedy. He longed for the kind of money that only the big sale of an Old Master can produce.

Van Meegeren knew how to make a painting appear old, and — this was the real trick — how to make it act old. Much more canny than Sakhai, he carefully purchased old rubbishy canvases, often attached to their original, hard-to-duplicate frames, painstakingly removed the image, painted a new one on the canvas, and then baked the result in an oven to get just the right amount of crackling to make the painting look its age.

In his day, van Meegeren had a good run passing off his fakes. He never sold a canvas directly to a customer; instead, he would approach a person of impeccable character, convince him that a penniless aristocrat wanted to part anonymously with his family's long-held treasure, and suggest that the man of high reputation market the picture out of the generosity of his heart. To make certain of his go-between's cooperation, van Meegeren always offered a substantial financial inducement.

Many eminent authorities churned out substantial pieces of scholarship arguing for the authenticity of van Meegeren's newly discovered Vermeers. Little did they realize that the wily Dutchman studied their writings carefully to discover what would be, for them, a true Vermeer. Many of his fakes were, in a sense, made to order.

Today, museum visitors possessing zero skills in art historical studies can easily identify a van Meegeren Vermeer as a fake: the emaciated, ghost-like figures in the faker's *Christ at Emmaus* are the obvious byproducts of a Netherlands on the verge of World War II.

When I look again at Brown's fakes, I become aware that he was not encumbered by the weight of his time as van Meegeren was. He had the rare capacity to place himself convincingly in the past. This is, for my purposes, a bad thing.

~

AFTER VAN GOGH'S death and subsequent meteoric rise in popularity, forgeries of his work proliferated. No one, for a time, was quite as grandiose in this practice as the preposterously named Otto Wacker. In the mid-Twenties, the former dancer set up as an art dealer and soon developed a reputation for selling works of impeccable quality and provenance. He placed a number of Van Goghs on offer, and quickly managed to convince many experts of the authenticity of the canvases. Wacker claimed that he bought the paintings from a Russian émigré who had transported them to Switzerland illegally and then commissioned an agent to sell them. The Russian could not be named for fear his relatives in the Soviet Union would suffer reprisals. The certificates of authenticity for the paintings were anything but; there was no real evidence as to the works' provenance. Yet despite the genuine *caveat emptor* nature of the situation, three major dealers purchased a number of the paintings.

For a while, Wacker dexterously skated on thin ice. The paintings were to be exhibited in January 1928 in Berlin in a grand exhibition to coincide with the publication of the standard catalogue of Van Gogh's work. But when the last four "discoveries" were delivered, they were denounced as fakes. Then thirty-three more were condemned. In April 1932, Wacker went on trial.

A nephew of Van Gogh stated that the family had never sold the paintings to the unknown Russian. A restorer testified that the pigments in the disputed paintings were not similar to Van Gogh's. Eventually, Wacker was sentenced to nineteen months in gaol.

Gabriel Brown would have been well aware of Otto Wacker and his tainted wares. Moreover, it is possible he had seen some of the fakes and profited from these viewings.

Chapter Twenty-One

℘❦

Lots of drawings: crucifixions, depositions, mums and kids, beggars, interiors, landscapes, canals, self-portraits. Quick drawings in bistre, mainly on eighteenth-century paper.

— TOM KEATING

I freely admit that I can be flippant, but the cheekiness of Keating is — and remains — puerile. In the above citation, he is boasting about the number of false Rembrandts that issued from his brush.

The happy-go-lucky surface conceals a deep-seated arrogance. To Keating, it was all an enormous practical joke. Like John Martin, he was born into impoverished circumstances. A house painter, he later became a restorer to help make ends meet. He saw little difference between the painting of houses and the painting of fine art. When he exhibited his own paintings, no one showed the slightest interest. Spitefully, he decided to become a sort of fine art vigilante who would take revenge on all the dealers and critics who connived to rig the market at the expense of naïve collectors and impoverished artists.

For a typical Rembrandt fake, Keating would mix his pigments with nuts, boil the mixture for ten or twelve hours, and then filter the results through silk. In this way, the colours would fade to the correct antique look.

Since he conceived of himself as a politically motivated anarchist, he would plant what he called "time-bombs." Sometimes, in his typically altruistic way, he would write phrases like *ever been had?* or *this is a fake*, or even a swear word, directly onto the canvas before starting work. He was told the messages, written in white lead paint, would show up under a picture if it were x-rayed. Often, he inserted a layer of glycerin under a layer of oil paint so that when the painting was sent out for cleaning it would disintegrate. This self-destruction would reveal that the painting was a forgery.

Of a very practical turn of mind, Keating would sometimes come across discarded frames with auction catalog numbers affixed to them. After telephoning the appropriate house to ask what painting had been housed in it, he would then prepare a canvas to match the empty frame.

Like John Martin, Tom Keating had an alternate identity. His was Sexton Blake, the poor man's Sherlock Holmes who began appearing in comic strips and novels in 1893. In Cockney rhyming slang, a Sexton Blake was a "fake," in contrast to Conan Doyle's "real" protagonist. Over two hundred authors have penned Sexton Blake narratives. That was part of Keating's ploy: there was no single genuine author to the Blake narrative, just as, in his twisted logic, no painting could be attributed to a single genuine artist.

In my study of the rogue originally named John Martin, I myself have become a sort of private investigator. Or am I a sham detective, trying to prize out someone else's sham existence?

The tone of Tom Keating's autobiography is completely devil-may-care; the man was genuinely proud of his accomplishments: "I have never made a secret of my ability to make fakes; I have boasted about it in pubs and at dinner parties. I've told almost everyone I've ever met about them. The only thing that amazes me is that I wasn't exposed in the press a lot sooner."

Had Brown been as arrogant as Keating? Did he also secretly hate the captains of industry and the aristocrats from whom he pried money?

THE PERSON WHO outed Keating, Geraldine Norman, was deeply sympathetic: "It can be argued that the blame for fakes lies primarily with the art market, not the faker, for it has lost touch with what art and the act of creation are all about. In the first place, a faker is creating art, not just something that looks deceptively like art. In the second, having allowed that artists should be untrammelled by conventions, traders should not complain too much about what they choose to create. The fact that a genuine Rembrandt may be worth a million pounds and a very good fake, say, fifty pounds, has nothing to do with their importance *as works of art*, i.e., the pure visual achievement; it has to do with the financial manipulation of an intellectual response to the art historical significance of Rembrandt and his *œuvre*."

Is Norman letting Keating completely off the hook? Is that what I should be doing for Brown? I don't think I'm capable of such generosity.

CHAPTER TWENTY-TWO

There are collectors who specialize in Keating fakes. Presumably, these people would have no interest in a genuine Rembrandt; only a fake Rembrandt by Tom would fit the bill. I can't quite get my head around this. It seems willfully deviant.

Where in all this does a genuine artist like Vermeer exist? Does it matter that he lived, breathed, sweated, and painted? Isn't he just someone to be exploited? After all, he's long dead. What's the harm?

Vermeer's existence is one enormous conundrum. He was baptized as Joannis in Delft in October 1632 and buried as Jan in the same city in December 1675. Those are the only certainties.

Joannis's father ran an inn and acted as a dealer in paintings. Twenty-one-year-old Joannis married Catharina Bolenes, the daughter of a rich Catholic widow, who might have insisted her son-in-law convert to her religion. He and his bride probably moved into the bride's mother's commodious house. The couple had fourteen children, four of whom died as infants.

No one knows if Vermeer trained as an artist. He could have

been self-taught; he may have learned from members of the Utrecht Carravagists; his teacher could have been a Catholic. On this score there is no end of speculation.

One person, a wealthy tradesman named Pieter van Rujiven, pinned down the market in Vermeers from the get-go. This man, enormously prescient, seems to have purchased the three canvases a year that the painter, a manifestly slow worker, produced.

In December 1675, Vermeer fell into a frenzy and died within thirty-six hours. Just after he died, an inventory was made of the eight rooms on the first floor of his residence. They were filled with paintings, drawings, clothes, chairs, and beds. The account of his studio is more detailed: two chairs, two easels, three palettes, ten canvases, a desk, an oak pull table, and a small wooden cupboard. There were approximately fifteen paintings left behind. They weren't worth much, which was part of the problem: Vermeer's widow was convinced that stress over a multitude of debts had killed her husband. Today, fifteen genuine Vermeers would be worth many kings' ransoms.

For a wide variety of reasons, there are only about thirty-five genuine Vermeers known to exist. There must be more pictures; there should be more pictures. Like nature, forgers hate a vacuum — though forgers especially hate one in which a great deal of money can be made.

The task is challenging, but it is possible to create a "new" Vermeer if one is clever enough to master the technological logistics, to reach a good understanding of how the Dutchman applied his paints, and to approximate the painter's small, delicate worldview. Someone like Gabriel Brown may have been capable of this task.

The buyer of a fake Vermeer might enjoy his purchase because he never realizes he has been tricked. After all, he has acquired the status of owning a Vermeer. But the thief knows his crime and must live with his sin. And where is the long-dead Vermeer — poverty-stricken and angst-filled — in the resulting muddle? He may be unaware of the crime, but his existence has been cruelly exploited. The artist's tomb in the Niewe Kerk in Delft is metaphorically vandalized, the bones scattered like pieces of garbage.

⁓

THE THOUGHT OF the injustice done Vermeer lowers my spirits. In my dreams, cannibals in eerie Rousseau-like jungles hunt me down. When Jacob stays on the weekend, I find it impossible to focus on him. If we go to the cinema, I cannot take in what I am seeing. When we take our usual jog through Regent's Park, and then on to the zoo, I remain silent. Usually the ridiculous-looking penguins lift my spirits, but this is no longer the case.

Usually Jacob chats away. He has an endless supply of jokes and witticisms with which to amuse me, but I can't crack even the semblance of a smile. Today he has had enough.

"You're a really crap dad. In case you haven't noticed."

I mumble an apology.

"It's too late to say you're sorry. You don't pay the slightest attention to anything I say."

"I'm really sorry. I haven't been myself recently."

"You don't connect with anyone. Not with me. Not with Mum."

"Your mother disconnected from me a long time before we separated."

"Is that what you think? Living with you is an existential dilemma."

I suspect Jacob is quoting Stella. There is, I admit, a lot of smoke where my ex-wife discerns a fire.

"I'm sorry for being such a bad father."

"You're not a bad father. You're a fake father."

I fidget a great deal during this unpleasant conversation and promise I will try to do better. Jacob shrugs, absolutely indifferent to any assurances I can offer.

CHAPTER TWENTY-THREE

I resolve to go full steam ahead with the Brown investigation. My problem is that I still do not know what my next step should be. I can't tell Amelia what I am up to. She would accuse me of having an untutored eye.

Although I continue to spend my weekdays at the London Library, I have reached a dead end in my reading about forgers. My email to Interpol headquarters in Lyon has produced a stock response. Although Interpol is interested in forgeries, its "target mission" is the recovery of stolen works of art. In other words, thievery in the manner I am investigating is a very low priority. Moreover, my enquiry about Gabriel Brown does not match up with any information they have on file. Unless I can provide them with more substantial leads, nothing can be done to assist me.

Weary, and more than a little depressed, I return to my enemy's home on a rainy Wednesday afternoon. Amongst the usual assortment of bills and junk mail in my email account, there is one that seizes my attention.

TO: Guy Boyd
FROM: A Would-Be Friend
RE: Gabriel Brown

Your request for information about Mr. Brown has come to
my attention. I may be able to assist you in your enquiries,
but you will have to follow my instructions to the letter. Do
you wish to proceed?

The note unnerves me. Has Interpol leaked my message? Or
has this person detected by other means my interest in Brown?
Has information on my computer been uncovered by spyware?

I am not by any means an expert on computers, but I do know
how to investigate an IP address. This one is in Ukraine, sent
from a server that is designed to conceal both the identities and
locations of its users. The person sending the message could be
anywhere in the world — most likely not Ukraine.

Having no other options at my disposal, I reply indicating
that I am open to any proposal he might make.

The response arrives ten minutes later.

Excellent! Further instructions will be issued soon.

I am now on pins and needles, and check my email every
half hour. There is nothing for two days, and then my marching
orders arrive:

You are to fly to Barcelona early next Tuesday morning.
You must be there to receive a further briefing at noon.
Bring your laptop with you, and be sure that your hotel has

> a wireless connection. You will be away from home
> for four days but in Barcelona for only two. Make
> appropriate arrangements.

That is it. Not having to worry about Jacob during the week, I quickly make a one-way EasyJet reservation for seven a.m. on Monday morning. Since I have been frugal with my advance, I book two nights at a four-star hotel highly recommended on TripAdvisor.

As usual, Amelia is supportive of my resolve to take a brief holiday. "You have been looking awfully wan recently. A trifle forlorn. I have heard that Barcelona is a very exciting place — probably much too 'with it' for the likes of me!"

AFTER ENDURING AN exceptionally cold and rainy April, even by London standards, the prospect of a few days in the sun cheers me. Queuing up at Stansted proves tolerable, though many of my fellow companions are football hooligans with ample brew on their breaths. The short flight is bumpy, but my spirits soar, and the glorious warm sun, even at eight in the morning, lifts me even further.

I immediately I check into my room and send an email indicating both my arrival and my readiness to take the next step. The response is quick.

> Excellent. Your hotel is within walking distance of the
> Gothic Quarter. At four o'clock this afternoon, you are to
> visit the nearby Museu Picasso. Be sure that you look
> carefully at every canvas. Before that, you might wish
> (you are under no obligation) to visit the Palau de la

Música Catalana, the Ramblas, and a Gaudí building
or two. Enjoy yourself.

How nice my unknown friend has become. He is, like every maître d' in London, exhorting me to have a nice day.

Having long harboured a desire to visit Gaudí's Casa Milà, I must admit to experiencing mild disappointment when my walk there on the Passeig de Gràcia is accompanied by a steady downpour, rather than the bright lemon-yellow sky that had greeted me two hours earlier.

The upside is that the entrance to the celebrated apartment building is not crowded with tourists. The small group waiting for the building to open is made up of seasoned sightseers who will not allow any kind of impediment to stand in the way of a chance to experience a cultural high.

As we wander into the elevator that takes us to the unoccupied flat we are allowed to visit, my companions speak in hushed and appreciative tones. All of us are enthusiastic admirers of Gaudí. The chairs, tables, even the bookcases have had the master's slight uneven curves applied to them. The headboard in the master bedroom even manages to look like butterfly wings. I am touched by the small, delicate pieces of clothing hung on a peg in a child's bedroom, and think fondly of Jacob back in London.

My visit to the roof is an exercise in agility, so slippery are the rain-splattered stairs and floors. A thick fog has now settled in and so only for a few minutes am I able to wander about marvelling at the chimneys — appropriately called *espanta bruixes,* or "witch scarers," by the locals — and the monster-like ventilation towers.

When the rain becomes even heavier, I taxi up to the Montjuïc district and the Joan Miró Foundation museum. Looking at one modern master might prepare me for another one later in the afternoon, I reason.

The white modular buildings and the accompanying large, spare white rooms make me feel warm and comfortable. The huge Calder mobiles are the only works of art I like here; they seem so pleased with themselves that I cannot resist applauding their ostentation. The simple colours of the paintings by the Spanish master Joan Miró are modestly beautiful.

OF PICASSO I have no doubts. He was a man who lived and breathed art. Some say he was a monster, a person who used others and then ruthlessly discarded them. Some claim he paid a heavy psychic price for his myriad accomplishments. The right adjective for him is protean: he was a man who was always reinventing himself — along with modern art, of course.

With some excitement, I take a taxi down to the Museu Picasso to carry out my mission. I feel like a schoolboy who has been given an assignment by a benign teacher. Very little light filters down Carrer Montcada that afternoon, and I now know why this section of the city is called the Gothic Quarter.

I am aware that Picasso spent his formative years in Barcelona, and I have read that the Museu consists of five adjoining medieval palaces. I resolve to perform my assigned role to perfection: I will take my time looking at everything on display, store everything in my internal hard drive, and be prepared to show my unknown master that I have completed my assignment diligently.

The genius of the great man is hard to locate in the Museu.

These are rooms filled, it could be argued, with augurs of the future — but I am the kind of museumgoer who is only interested in fulfillment, not promise. Most of what I see is early work, in which I am supposed to find reflections of Picasso's subsequent genius. I do not give a toss about *La Primera Communión*, which he painted at the age of fifteen.

Good intentions do not assist me, and I soon find myself overcome by soul-drenching weariness. My mind wanders. I find it difficult to keep my eyes open and frequently stifle yawns. What if my email supervisor is following me around the rooms or observing me on cctv? I draw my shoulders up and resolve to be the best possible imitation of a diligent student I can be.

The early work at the Museu is finally relieved by a few third-rate paintings from Picasso's subsequent years. Then follow the *Pichones* paintings, pictures I detest as I loathe pigeons.

Then there are the *Meninas* (*Handmaidens*) studies. The forty-five canvases grip me. My eyes are wide open again.

I have seen many reproductions of Velázquez's 1656 masterpiece *Las Meninas*, in which the five-year-old Infanta Margarita is shown surrounded by a wide assortment of ladies-in-waiting, a mastiff, and a painter who works on an easel behind this assemblage and gazes at his subjects from behind. Picasso's response to Velázquez's masterpiece is visceral — gut-wrenching, I would say. He completely breaks rank with the aristocratic sedateness of his predecessor. Though Picasso may have been in awe, it did not prevent him from unleashing a barrage of riotously coloured, energy-filled canvases which parody and imitate Velázquez. He was intent on showing how the older artist got it all wrong. No more demure saccharine-looking

Infantas for Picasso. For him she becomes the excuse for every stylistic device known to him — and he knew a great many. In several, she is a masterpiece of cubist reinvention.

Is this reimagination or rejection? A great deal of both, I tell myself. I study these canvases diligently, quite certain they are intended to be the subject of my investigation.

AFTER TWO HOURS, I experience museum cardiac arrest and go back to my hotel room. There may be a quiz for me to complete. After downing two whiskeys from the mini-bar and taking two minutes to stare out the window, I turn on my computer. Of course there is an email.

> You have fulfilled the first part of your assignment nobly. Congratulations. You should now book an air ticket to Madrid for this evening and, after careful consideration, arrange for a room at a hotel near the Prado. Instructions will follow as soon as you arrive at your hotel.

So, I assure myself, I have playacted perfectly. Others might rightly claim that I have become the perfect poodle. To be honest, I do not appreciate being dispatched like a parcel from destination to destination.

CHAPTER TWENTY-FOUR

𝕰

After the short flight to Madrid, a taxi takes me to my hotel, which fronts onto the Plaza Mayor. It is nine o'clock, but not many tourists have strolled out for their evening meal. Since I do not wish to be fashionably early, I stroll up and down the plaza. I have no difficulty imagining the spectacles that once took place in this very spot: the bullfights, the Inquisition trials, the executions. Still too early to find a suitable *mesón*, I return to my room and turn on my computer. Once again, through the miracle of in-room WiFi, a message is waiting.

> Delighted you have reached Madrid. Take it easy this evening. You have a busy day ahead of you. Be at the Prado at opening time (9 a.m.) tomorrow. Spend exactly two hours there. Then stroll back to your room for further instructions.

The rebellious streak in me is beginning to activate, but I cannot react angrily to the military-style, condescension-laden regimen imposed by my correspondent. Though I had been convinced a visit to the Prado would figure in his plans, I was not given precise instructions as to what I should look at there. I had, and have, the freedom to choose for myself. Of course I want to see *Las Meninas*. Perhaps my usually dictatorial friend does not wish to insult my intelligence by making such an obvious suggestion?

I resolve to look at as much Spanish painting as possible, especially the Goyas and El Grecos. If that does not suit my self-anointed boss, *tant pis*!

I do not sleep well, a real toss-and-turn night. What madness have I unleashed? What kind of Pandora's box have I opened? I should be back in London looking after my son, not embarking on a wild goose chase.

At seven I am in the breakfast room when it opens to down two cups of coffee, before beginning my stroll in the direction of the Prado.

IN CONTRAST TO Barcelona, Madrid is more self-assured. It does not attempt to act charming — it *is* charming. The buildings on my route are more restrained than comparable ones in Barcelona, and the boulevards are just as wide but not as ostentatious. I like that: the city as a subdued spectacle.

As I approach the Museo Thyssen-Bornemisza, I wonder if I will be required to pop in there this afternoon to see the greatest private art collection open to the public. Or will I be sent a bit further afield to the Reina Sofía to take in *Guernica*? Had Gabriel ever sold anything to Baron Heinrich Thyssen-Bornemisza? Had Gabriel targeted the Baron's wife, a former Miss Spain named Carmen Cervera, as a likely dupe? Her collection is also on display.

As I pass through the lush park that leads to the Prado, such venal thoughts gradually desert me. I am calmed by Parque del Buen Retiro's vast expanses of green. I am far too early for the street musicians, jugglers, fortunetellers, and clowns who will give the place its true carnival atmosphere in a few hours, but there are small tranquil lakes, and squealing children accompanied by nursemaids.

I enter the Prado at the Goya entrance with my spirits raised. Churlishly, I walk past the Titians and the Tintorettos in the Italian galleries, whisk by the Rubens gallery, even skip the Rembrandt self-portraits, and head for the Riberas, Murillos, and the forty-odd Velázquezes. Gabriel had sold two Velázquezes to the Prado: am I looking at either of them? If so, are they fakes?

Finally I reach *Las Meninas*. What an arrogant show-off Velázquez was! And why not, with his phenomenal talent? The Infanta stands daintily arrayed before the spectator, her head turned ever so coyly to the right. Two maids attend to her needs, while the other four seem more intrigued by the spectator than by the princess. A man at an easel — Velázquez himself — is at work. In the far reaches of the room stands Felipe IV, the Infanta's father and the artist's patron, the person who has brought all of these people together. It is a tricky set-up to say the least: the Infanta places herself on display for the artist's benefit, the artist portrays himself as the diligent observer, and the Infanta and the painter are both being scrutinized by the King.

In addition to all the other talents Nature had showered upon him, Velázquez must have had a prodigious intellect. Here, simply put, is a painting analyzing the role of the artist in society. Does the artist simply kowtow to the rich and powerful? Or is the artist supremely aware that he must charm the rich and powerful in order to survive? Is this painting an act of obeisance? Or is the painter highlighting the fact that all artists must subdue any sense they have of themselves as individuals in the service of those who pay the bills?

No wonder Picasso drew and re-drew this painting over and over again. One who conceives of himself as a genius might still be shaken by a greater genius, and might try to find a way to subvert this other claimant. Was Picasso trying to steal Velázquez's thunder? Or was he trying to catch the same thunderbolts that had struck the earlier artist? *Las Meninas* displays a greatness I know I can never touch. I know why Picasso had been so jealous of it.

Suddenly my head begins to spin violently. I am used to looking at masterpieces in museums, being seduced by their charms, musing about them, and, then, within an hour, being overcome with boredom. Now, being required to inspect paintings and to piece together what I see, I am overwhelmed.

I cannot not leave without looking at the Goyas, so I walk down to the gallery that contains the Black Paintings. The seven dark, violence-filled images had been painted directly on the walls of the Quinta del Sordo, the artist's home on the banks of the Manzanares River. Their tar-coloured blacks, cold whites, and blood reds make me feel even more frenzied and delirious.

Who is the viewer who can prevent himself from being repulsed by *Saturn Devouring His Son*, surely the most powerful image of parental failure ever painted? Even on a good day, the sight of the fear-crazed tyrant, convinced that one of his children will usurp his throne, cannibalizing his newborn son would nauseate me. The painting reminds any well-meaning parent that he must take good care of the children entrusted to him. I experience more than a tinge of guilt: I have not been paying enough attention to Jacob.

Overwhelmed. That seems a mild word to describe the horrible cacophony of emotions that invade my soul. I have never felt as confused as I do in the few minutes it takes me to walk up the stairs, find the exit, and breathe fresh air. I remain frightened by the image of Saturn, afraid of getting in touch with the most selfish parts of myself.

Chapter Twenty-Five

As I walk back to my hotel room, and towards the new email directive that will surely confront me, I realize I have not a clue as to the cat-and-mouse game in which I have become involved. I am aware of my status as a mouse; but why did the cat bother to get in touch with me? Presumably I will learn the secret of Gabriel Brown's existence as a forger, but I now entertain serious doubts that anything significant will be revealed.

The day is one worthy enough to be called perfect. Culture-pursuing tourists make the rounds from the Prado to the Thyssen to the Reina Sofía. They are in paradise: beautiful weather outside, sublime works of art inside. They have a sated look on their faces; for them, no further human bliss exists. The residents of Madrid, smartly dressed, promenade with their heads held high. They have the appearance of male peacocks in the mating season: *our city has a spectacular beauty*, their postures announce. Children frolic in nearby Balboa Park. Many of the girls practice hopscotch. I even witness one or two expert cartwheels.

I do not fancy returning to my hermetically sealed, overly air-conditioned room, and I do not wish to take a further step in my detective work. But when I return, the directive in the new message startles me:

> Tomorrow morning you will take a taxi to the Museo
> Sorolla at General Martínez Campos. Your trip will take
> approximately a half hour. Be sure you arrive at 9:30 when
> the museum opens its doors. Look carefully. Take exactly
> two hours. Then visit the gardens.

In haste, I turn to my guidebook. Museo Sorolla has a cursory entry under *Worth Noting*: "See the world through the exceptional eye of Spain's most famous Impressionist painter, Joaquín Sorolla (1863–1923), who worked most of his life at the home and garden he designed." Famous in Spain — but did anyone outside the Iberian Peninsula know anything about him?

That evening, I delve further into the streets near my hotel. Under a moonlit sky, tourists and Spaniards converge upon the wide assortment of open-air restaurants. Children are eager participants at many tables. For them, eating a meal means merrymaking. I have never before witnessed joy as pure as that which emanates from these celebrants. I want to be carried away by these feelings, but cannot. Maybe if I were with Jacob I could muster a semblance of joy-filled spontaneity. I walk away from the revels, feeling a bit like the Grendel monster cast into the darkness.

My spirits are lifted when I come upon the tall, floodlit vertical garden of the CaixaForum. Despite all the impediments of gravity, a profusion of flowers, shrubs, and small trees grow heavenwards. They are survivors. *If this miserable existence is given to us,* they have determined, *we will make the best of it. If our human masters subject us to unnatural torment, we will defy them.*

⁓

THE DRIVE TO Museo Sorolla is a long one. I am no longer in tourist Madrid. Real Spaniards live in the high-rises that soar, canyon-like, in this section of the city. Because the Museo is surrounded front and back by apartment buildings, I do not see it at first. But there it is: a stately cream-coloured palazzo with an elegant front garden.

Except for the ticket seller and the other attendants, one could almost imagine oneself having popped in for a morning coffee at a rich man's home. Sorolla was a great success in his lifetime. The living and dining rooms are furnished in a combination of Art Nouveau and Art Deco trappings that were inordinately expensive in the owner's lifetime and are now priceless. They bespeak taste, elegance, and ostentation.

Most of the main floor is given over to the great man's studio at the front. Two storeys high, it was designed to welcome in as much light as possible, as it does today.

Because it has been left as it was when he died, I can imagine the painter in this room. There is no hint of disarray, nor the remains of unfinished projects, and I know right away that Sorolla was a man who would not tolerate disorder. He did not possess the penchant for mess that a genius dervish like Picasso relished.

Sorolla canvases accompany me as I wander the rooms, make my way up the elegant staircase, and walk through the spacious bedrooms. He often painted his wife and children playing on various beaches. There is an arresting picture of the painter's wife in bed, smiling benignly at a newborn infant daughter resting securely on a pillow beside her. In another, a naked eight- or nine-year-old boy positions his toy sailboat in the water.

The large images, filled with mellow gold sunlight, inviting deep ocean blues, and the gently billowing clothes of children, are records of a supremely happy life. The painter had been a contented man. If one thinks of works of art only as creations wrested from suffering and deprivation, Sorolla provides convincing evidence to the contrary.

I had entered the Museo in a turbulent state, but I leave feeling bathed in the milk of human kindness. What an incredible turnaround, I muse. I wander to a bench where I can behold the sun bestowing its attention upon the house, before teasingly withdrawing it again. I sit there for at least ten minutes before I notice a man at the other end of the bench. He is small and wizened, perhaps eighty years of age, and dressed neatly in suit and tie.

Having noticed my attention, the man stands up, shakes himself slightly, and moves towards me. "You don't mind if I sit down beside you, Mr. Boyd? I think we can now dispense with emails. I have many qualms about modern technology."

I should not have been surprised. "So you are my mysterious correspondent?"

"The very same. My given name is Diego. I hope you will not mind if I do not share my surname with you. "

"I have in the last little while become quite used to cloaks and daggers. I have no objection."

"There is some bitterness in your voice. I am here to

remove it."

"I still don't understand why you have subjected me to these strange manoeuvres."

Diego has a wonderful smile. His face lights up, and he looks me in the eye. "Only by asking you to visit a few places first could I impart what little knowledge, and perhaps wisdom, I possess."

DIEGO IS FORMERLY of Interpol, so newly retired that he has seen my enquiry about Gabriel Brown. His former colleagues in Lyon are powerless to assist me, and he should not be sharing secrets. However, my request for help intrigued him — he was, for many years, in charge of the Brown dossier.

"I can tell you some things of interest. Unofficially, of course."

I nod in agreement. What else can I do?

"Your method of tracking Brown is amazing. You have used your eyes. For more than forty years I thought I was the only one who had glimpsed that man's soul. I knew I had to meet you. First, congratulations are in order. Second, I must tell you that the Brown situation is unique."

For the next hour, Diego provides me with an account of his role at Interpol. Most of the Fine Arts team's resources are devoted to the recovery of stolen property, especially from museums. Not much funding is provided for uncovering those who traffic in forgeries — a fact that Diego points out is unfortunately well known to those who produce and sell fakes. A certain kind of immunity from prosecution is bestowed upon them.

Diego devoted most of his career to tracking down what he terms "spectacular heists." More interested than most of his colleagues in the fine arts, he became a specialist in investigating forgers. It was a daunting prospect, because those who are adept at making fakes do not usually get caught — an observation particularly true of Gabriel Brown.

Diego's suspicions were first aroused in 1977, when the famous London dealer sold a Velázquez to the Prado. Having returned home on leave, Diego saw the announcement in newspapers and on television about the acquisition of a previously unknown work by the master. The subject and its iconography, the Assumption of the Virgin, were unusual for the artist; they were Murillo territory.

Diego arranged to be invited to the unveiling of the painting, at a reception attended by the King and Queen. When he arrived at the event, Diego immediately recognized Brown. "He had a genuinely elegant look to him. Some people would say he looked like an aristocrat. That was true. When he was presented to Juan Carlos and Sofía, he had an air of modesty about him. He acted like someone who was most grateful to be received, but carried himself like someone who deserved to be received. I liked him right away. Of the painting, I had my doubts. Despite its idiosyncrasies, it looked too much like a Velázquez; it was a canvas that proclaimed itself too ostentatiously. I wondered if it was a fake.

"After that encounter, I paid attention whenever Brown's name appeared in the media. I assembled a portfolio of what I could discover about his previous sales. I searched for, but never came upon, any sort of complaint lodged against him. Your email riveted me, because you were the first person to suggest that the famous dealer was a fraud."

"I have no evidence," I confess. "In researching his biography, I looked at many photographs of him and the pictures he sold. It was in a blinding flash that I realized he had painted all the canvases in his twenty-fifth-anniversary prospectus. The man's conceit enraged me."

"You are almost certainly correct, although your methodology would be considered suspect by many. I, on the other hand, think you have the eyes of a genuine connoisseur. Let's push such considerations aside for the moment. Let me tell you what I discovered.

"There is too much perfection in some of the unknown Rembrandts, Vermeers, and Leonardos that Brown discovered. Perfection is not a human trait, but one cultivated by counterfeiters. In their pursuit of it, they sometimes stumble.

"Brown never came upon pictures that were known to have existed and then disappeared. Instead, he had the knack of nosing out pictures that were never known to exist. There are such people outside of forgers, genuine art detectives — that was certainly Brown's reputation.

"I noticed a pattern in his history of discovering masterpieces. He would leave his gallery for two or three weeks on his legendary searches, not interviewing art historians or spending time in any archive, but rather holing up in Paris, and always at the same five-star hotel. There, he would take the Métro in the morning and disappear. I had him followed once or twice, but he was far too clever for his pursuers."

"So what was he doing in Paris?"

"I later learned that he was in contact with an atelier that specialized in the production of forgeries. The owner of the atelier and his assistants provided him with the correct canvas, paints, and other ancillary materials.

"If you know what you are about, you can purchase extremely old canvases containing third- and fourth-rate pictures. Carefully strip away the paint and you have a genuinely old surface upon which to work. You can then buy the ingredients used to make up, say, the oil paints of an Italian Renaissance canvas, and mix them so the exact colours are replicated. There are compounds that assist in giving the finished painting the appearance of having been painted centuries earlier. The technological advances made by forgers in the past thirty years are nothing short of miraculous."

I am not terribly surprised by these revelations. The question for me remains why Brown would do such things.

"You and I still have many things to ponder," Diego observes. "It is well past noon, and you are probably hungry. Shall we meet this evening? I can be at your hotel at nine o'clock." He stands up, shakes my hand, and vanishes.

CHAPTER TWENTY-SIX

D iego has not yet informed me of the purpose of my various museum experiences. Perhaps he wants to give me the afternoon to grapple with the apparent method in his madness.

Velázquez had intimidated Picasso. The latter attempted all his various reworkings of *Las Meninas* in order to rid himself of this insecurity. An old-fashioned testosterone-induced pissing contest? Or, to place it a kinder light, imitation as the sincerest form of flattery?

Sorolla, on the other hand, was a very unusual man: the artist as non-neurotic. He lived a contented life. He took great joy in his family, was extraordinarily successful, and created a home in which his art reigned supreme. Unlike his fellow countrymen, Picasso and Velázquez, he has not been accorded posthumous international fame — he is simply not in their league — but I somehow doubt this would have bothered him.

I am supposed to establish a link that has previously evaded me but, beyond the obvious, I can't make any headway. Diego very much enjoys the role of teacher, and I have no doubt he has a lesson carefully planned for me.

TRUE TO HIS word, Diego is waiting for me in the foyer of my hotel at the appointed hour. He suggests we stroll to Restaurante Ølsen on Calle del Prado. "Perhaps you are sated with Spanish cuisine and might like to try something Scandinavian?" I have no objection. "The cuisine at Ølsen is refreshingly non-Iberian, and, moreover, they have a wide assortment of vodkas, my favourite drink."

The restaurant sports an austere but pleasant teak-and-chrome interior, and also happens to offer venison, a choice to which we both respond enthusiastically. We each down vodka cocktails before Diego turns his attention to the reason for my presence in Spain.

"We could have spoken on the phone, but I am not sure you would have understood me unless you had taken some circumstances into account."

"Circumstances? You asked me to look at pictures."

"I requested that you pay attention to certain images so that you could come to an appreciation of what is involved in creativity. Otherwise, you could not understand Brown."

"I haven't the slightest idea what you're talking about."

Unfazed, he gives me a broad smile. "In Barcelona you saw how Picasso wrestled with Velázquez. At the Prado, you beheld the painting that niggled Picasso so deeply. I asked you to visit Sorolla's home so that you could come into contact with a man who had none of Picasso's neurotic impulses. In all three places, you beheld countrymen of mine who dedicated their lives to art. In the case of the two men from the twentieth century, you witnessed very different results. It was Picasso who has survived, and will continue to do so. No one really cares about Sorolla.

"Many points could be made, perhaps, but I wanted you to be aware that if a person is born to be an artist, he must follow that profession — no matter what the results are. Something in him will be killed off unless he does so."

"What does this have to do with Brown?"

"He was an artist. As a person he was much more a Sorolla than a Picasso. He had to paint, but he knew that he possessed little or no claim to originality or genius. Sorolla accepted his fate: he produced beautiful paintings that pleased him, and he became prosperous. Brown, I suspect, was rage-filled. He had the most perfect understanding of technique, accompanied by consummate practical brilliance. He was a master of the grammar of art. But he did not have anything original to say. I suspect that is the reason he made his counterfeits."

"He also made them to enrich himself."

"That is true, but I think you are missing the essential ingredients in his makeup. By my count, most of the paintings sold by Brown were genuine. He was a superb detective, someone who possessed the skills of a bloodhound in nosing out forgotten masterpieces."

"All of the paintings in the twenty-fifth-anniversary prospectus are fakes."

"He intended that exhibition to be the single great display of his cunning mastery of the art world. His career as a forger of Old Masters might only have been a brief one, from about 1972 to 1980. Most of the time, he was an honest businessman whose inner demons told him he had the soul of a great artist."

"He was no such thing. He was a mere imitator."

"That was the rub. Deprived of originality, he nevertheless had to paint."

"Suppose you are correct. Don't you still think he should be exposed?"

"That decision I will leave in your hands. I must tell you that when I contemplate Brown and look at the 'recreations' he made, I am filled with a sense of wonder. He was not like those nefarious thieves who burgled the Isabella Stewart Gardner Museum in Boston in 1990, who stole thirteen canvases, including Vermeer's *The Concert*, by cutting them out of their frames.

"Who are the genuine criminals? The man who lovingly created a painting the master could be proud of? Or the two thieves who ripped Mrs. Gardner's paintings from their frames? Or those who store works of art as if they are bars of gold?"

Diego places his hands out in front of him, then joins them together as if in prayer. He looks me up and down. "I am reminded of the New Testament story of the men about to stone the woman found guilty of adultery. Christ observed: 'He that is without sin, let him cast the first stone.' Who among us is not guilty of some sort of duplicity?"

PART FOUR

REVERBERATIONS

CHAPTER TWENTY-SEVEN

Sympathy for Gabriel Brown is second nature to Amelia and Diego. But for me he remains a person who grew rich through deception. He did not practise simple sleights of hand the way a magician does. He was an alchemist turning dross into gold.

I don't know if I care that Brown deceived collectors and curators. *Caveat emptor.* But what about the basic chicanery? My bourgeois sense of right and wrong has been violated. Does it matter to me that Brown was a would-be artist, technically gifted but devoid of vision? Many of us would like to be Hamlet; if we're lucky, we settle for being Rosencrantz or Guildenstern. As a writer, I have long accepted that I have a minor voice.

But the voice is mine. I don't want someone else's.

I have been trying with considerable difficulty to form a bond with Brown, the subject of my putative biography, yet every time I inch forward he forces me to slip backwards. The whole process of life writing has become a game of snakes and ladders.

Unlike Gabriel Brown, I had a normal neurotic upbringing. My parents may have been overprotective, but they made it clear they had high expectations for me, their only child. I lost the wish to please at about the age of ten, which essentially constituted my rebellion against them. Privately, they must have thought I did not show much backbone. I did well enough at school and, later, at university, but I was not what anyone would call an overachiever — or even an achiever. Life carried me along.

Brown was very different. He was a driven man, the pauper who pushes himself to prove that he deserves admiration, if not love. Unlike me, he was an ambitious man. Unlike me, he had scores to settle for life's injustices. He made a calculated assault on life, whereas I have always lacked both courage and conviction.

I am the lesser. Brown is the greater. He made sure his reach did not exceed his grasp.

～

FOR THE PAST decade, my father's time has been consumed by his hobby of making antique furniture. He owns facsimiles of the surviving Chippendale and Hepplewhite catalogues and has books on the various techniques employed by those two great designers at their workshops. He purchases the finest wood, some of it quite old, and he knows how to reconstruct the various glues used in the late eighteenth and early nineteenth centuries.

The sitting room, the dining room, and the three bedrooms of my parents' home are filled with my father's work. There is, for example, a grand display cabinet in the sitting room made from the finest cherry wood obtainable; the glass is two centuries old, having been removed from some nondescript old object. The joins of the wood — something which Dad talks about in painstaking, boring detail — are done to the most exacting standards. His pieces of furniture could pass for genuine antiques, if not for the fact that my father signs each unobtrusively.

He has never seemed the slightest bit aware how out of place the antiques look in a suburban bungalow. All of Dad's pieces of furniture are intended for large, spacious rooms; in my parents' home they have no breathing space.

For years, I thought my father's hobby was a waste of time. He and Mum could afford a high-end reproduction or two, although they could never afford even, say, a genuine small Hepplewhite card table. Why bother to make an authentic copy of something that already exists?

Now I can see that the effort gives my father pleasure. His hobby provides a framework in which to exercise his creativity, his artistic impulses channeled into various pieces of furniture. Diego took a similar view when told me about Brown's forgeries. But unlike Brown, my father would never attempt to have one of his pieces pass muster as the "real thing" on the Antiques Roadshow. He does not sell them. They have never been constructed to deceive anyone.

CHAPTER TWENTY-EIGHT

Gabriel Brown: 1967–1986

Gabriel is bored. Whole days are simply expanses of time in which, robot-like, he looks at pictures, buys some, talks to customers on the phone, greets customers at the gallery, attends to correspondence, and places calls to various parts of the Continent to follow up on leads.

He never thinks of Canada except for when customers ask if he is American. In such instances, he assures them he was born in Canada. This is almost comforting news to the questioners, who are pleased not to have to deal with a Yank. Canada is viewed as a subjected nation, whereas America is made up of bumptious upstarts.

Material prosperity has not eluded him. He is comfortably off. He has furnished his home with Bauhaus-inspired furniture, mirrors, curtains, and rugs. Fellow dealers who specialize in contemporary prints have provided him with Picassos, Chagalls, Braques, and other living masters at bargain prices.

He enjoys the company of various lady friends, but he

deems himself a person both unwilling and unable to maintain a steady relationship. "I am essentially a loner," he tells himself for comfort. For him, such rugged individualism is a style of life suited for only a few brave souls.

Gabriel begins to look back wistfully and nostalgically at the Krieghoff forgeries he completed in Canada before the War. He allows himself to think of that time as a halcyon period, days when he lived in a devil-may-care manner. He does not give much thought to the fact that he had barely escaped gaol. He wants to be young again. Perhaps this is the beginning of a mid-life crisis?

When he decides to return to his old vocation as a forger, he becomes exceptionally circumspect. In conversations with other dealers, he often hears tell of those who deal in stolen or forged goods, and he listens intently for those whom he might make use of in his new resolve. He keeps his own mouth firmly shut.

The name Rufus O'Brian comes up in several contexts. At a party, Gabriel overhears the Dutch Renaissance expert for Sotheby's whispering to his counterpart at Christie's that O'Brian might be a slippery character: "He offers us awfully good things, but I'm not sure about his provenances." A few days later at lunch he hears O'Brian characterized as the seller of "amazingly good things." Another time, Gabriel visits a fellow dealer and notices the dealer's address book open at his desk. O'Brian's address and phone number in Paris are entered; next to them is a huge question mark. Gabriel memorizes the information.

He discovers that Rufus O'Brian is a fellow Canadian, aged forty, and a buyer and seller of Old Masters. Apparently he does not have a gallery, working instead from his flat in the sixteenth arrondissement. Further delving reveals that O'Brian comes from a wealthy Anglophone family from Montreal, was born in Westmount, attended McGill, and then, at the age of twenty-two, set off for France, were he has lived for eighteen years. He is sufficiently wealthy that he does not need to work, and dabbles in art as a form of amusement.

This sounds like a man after my own heart, Gabriel tells himself.

SHORT ON LOOKS but endowed with charisma: this is Gabriel's initial assessment of O'Brian, whose full beard and piercing brown eyes are offset by his obese and five-foot-tall frame. He is one of those rare creatures who, unfortunately, looks as round as he is high. As if aware that he needs a mighty weapon in his arsenal, O'Brian exudes a gentle friendliness, coupled with exuberant intellectual prowess.

O'Brian's flat is vast. The two sitting rooms are large, and Gabriel guesses there are at least four bedrooms. The living spaces are furnished grandly in authentic Louis XIV side tables, desks, and chairs. The upholstered furniture is modern but designed to blend in with the antique pieces. The walls are covered by Boucher and Fragonard drawings, each of which is shown to best advantage in a period frame.

"As you can see, I only have a few drawings at the moment," O'Brian indicates, as he hands Gabriel the requested gin and tonic.

They make small chat for about ten minutes before Gabriel decides to broach the reason for his visit.

"I have heard your name mentioned in several contexts."

"It's good that my name crops up in London, I suppose."

"For my purposes, excellent."

"You intrigue me."

"In the past month I have become convinced that you and I share many things in common, beside our place of birth. I suspect that you have invented a past for yourself. So have I."

If he is shocked by the assertion, O'Brian does not betray it.

Gabriel continues. "I am in need of locating someone who can assist me in the manufacturing of Old Masters. I suspect you can help me in this endeavour."

"You wish to make them yourself?"

"In Canada, before the War, that was how I earned my living."

"Have you been selling such contraband at your gallery?"

"No. I wish to begin a new phase in my career."

O'Brian smiles broadly. "All the drawings you see here are genuine, but I have sometimes offered a few rediscovered treasures on the market from time to time."

"I was certain that was the case."

"If we are to become partners in your new endeavour, there are several ground rules that must be observed."

O'BRIAN IS PAINSTAKING in laying out how they will proceed. In the future, they will only communicate using phone boxes and postcards. If one wishes to contact the other, he will send a postcard indicating a number and a time. The respondent will then call at the appointed hour. Gabriel will inform O'Brian which artist he wants to fake, the exact year to which the painting should be attributed, its exact size, and the colours to be employed. O'Brian will provide Gabriel with a studio — an empty apartment — in which to paint. He will also provide all materials: authentic canvases and paints manufactured in accordance with the date of the forgery. Only when the painting is completed will Gabriel contact O'Brian, who will supply a suitable frame and then arrange to have the painting transported to London.

For each painting, an upfront advance of £10,000 is required. When work is completed, Gabriel will pay any balance owing. Upon sale, O'Brian is to receive thirty-five per cent of that amount.

AND SO GABRIEL Brown sets himself up again in the forgery business. During his trips to Paris, Brown stays at George V. Although the apartments used as studios are always changed, O'Brian suggests that, in the unlikely event he is being followed, Brown is to take a circuitous route by Métro to the assigned studio. One can never be too careful.

Even without the injunction from O'Brian, Gabriel is cautious. He remembers how close he came to getting caught in Canada.

A SIGNIFICANT NUMBER of Gabriel's clients are people who, though born into a high caste, given an excellent education, and possessed of vast holdings of real estate, are inherently kindly and tell themselves: if the grace of God had not been bestowed upon me, I could have wound up considerably down the ladder.

Then there are those who have, by dint of hard work and gritty determination, achieved great wealth. Some of these persons carry humble origins well. Not a hint of pretentiousness invades their countenances or their behaviour.

Finally, there are those for whom one can never do enough. A sense of *noblesse oblige* has escaped their existences. Nothing is never good enough for them. Everyone is scheming to do them in. To such people, Gabriel is a mere factotum who is to do exactly what is required. Anything less is a betrayal of the conventions that exist between master and servant.

One such customer is Lady Millicent: well born, but to a family that was forced to marry her off to a lowborn number cruncher who had made a vast fortune in the city. In private life, Lady Millicent is Mrs. Smith. She does not care for her married name and always insists on being addressed by the name with which she was born. Gabriel always calls her "madam" or "ma'am."

Tall and decidedly willowy, Lady Millicent is a familiar figure in Mayfair, Bond Street, and Pall Mall. She is renowned for her bad temper, which she displays to anyone who shows the slightest inclination to not do immediately what she commands.

Though Gabriel's ever-ready smile is difficult at first for the lady to deny, and though she also appreciates the frequent nods he bestows in her direction, even his eager friendliness eventually irritates her.

Unfortunately, Lady Millicent either wants canvases that do not exist as far as anyone knows, or she hankers for a Romney at the National Gallery, or a Stubbs ensconced in a neighbouring estate in Hampshire. "I don't see why there are no extant Gainsborough paintings of noblewomen that I can acquire. The auction houses have nothing of interest. You dealers are hopeless. All the best things have gone to the United States to the likes of Frick, Morgan, and Huntington."

If his would-be customer annoys Gabriel, he never shows it. He simply tells the noble lady that he will give the matter his full attention.

A year later, he is able to offer her the perfect Gainsborough. The full-length portrait splendidly displays a red-haired, green-eyed woman with exceedingly sharp features. The nose is aquiline but long; the neck juts out very noticeably; deep worry lines and a furrowed brow are much in evidence. Everyone who sees the painting considers it repulsive.

Lady Millicent, however, is smitten. She does not quibble about the heavy asking price or enquire too deeply about the picture's provenance. She listens intently when Brown tells her about the distressed family in Northamptonshire who have decided, after much anguish, to part with a family heirloom.

Lady Millicent's new painting provides much fodder for discussion at dinner parties: "The woman in the picture looks like her. Mr. Brown could not have found a better picture if he had ordered it custom made."

~

THEN THERE IS Sir George Armstrong, the oil magnate. In retirement, he grows roses and collects paintings. Whereas he has several thousand different varieties of roses on his estate in Cornwall, Armstrong's paintings are few. Because they "have to be the best out there," he only owns four "world-class" pictures: a Rembrandt, a Renoir, a Picasso, and a Gauguin.

Armstrong summons Gabriel to his estate and announces that the Gauguin, a large Tahiti canvas, requires a companion Van Gogh. After the War, many works by the Dutchman made their way into auction houses, but none of them are really what Armstrong wants. They do not look like *Starry Night*; none have enough flowers in them; the portraits are, in his view, drab and listless. "If you can find me what I like — what I know in my heart of hearts has to exist — you can name your price."

Patiently, Gabriel tells the old man that the requisite picture might have never existed or, if it does, it might have been destroyed.

"Nonsense. I have read the correspondence between Vincent and Theo, and I know that Vincent must have painted the picture I envision in my mind's eye. I know the kind of Van Gogh I am destined to purchase."

Gabriel gives Armstrong his brightest, clearest smile. "Many great pictures have made their way into Christie's and Sotheby's. Surely one of them would have satisfied you?"

The old man shakes his head.

Gabriel then argues, "Over the past five years, I have shown you photographs of five extraordinary specimens, all from the Arles period, and none suits you. They are still available."

In this instance, Mr. Armstrong is oblivious to both reason and charm, and the Van Goghs — of Gabriel's devising — slip into oblivion.

～

BROWN'S CAREER AS a forger did not last long, perhaps just over a decade. In his second stint as a faker, he probably did no more than a hundred paintings — less than twenty percent of what he sold over his long career as a purveyor of Old Masters.

Why did he quit a second time? Probably the same motivation that drew him to resume that career in the first place: boredom. It was all so easy. The headlines about O'Brian's arrest in 1981 and subsequent trial may have also induced him to abandon his criminal ways.

Nevertheless, the twenty-fifth-anniversary exhibition and its accompanying prospectus display a bold arrogance. Here was a man who stood by his achievements and wanted others to notice them — a man who kidded himself that he was performing a virtuous act by expanding the canons of some of the geniuses in the pantheon of Western artists.

Chapter Twenty-Nine

M y newest version of the biography comes close to a whitewash. I maintain the stance of an objective recorder of
Brown's existence, to allow readers the space in which to reach
their own conclusions — but in doing so, I am being untrue
to myself.

Moreover, I am left with a minuscule volume. Duval had
said a short text — what is sometimes contemptuously called
potted biography — would be entirely acceptable; he intends
many pages of colour reproductions, and to include the full
text of Brown's twenty-fifth-anniversary exhibition catalogue.
I don't think he has the slightest notion of how meagre and
how scandalous my dredging will be.

Even with modest expectations, I doubt Duval will welcome
a memorial of someone's life that reveals the subject was an
imposter and a forger. The art-historical fraternity would be
shocked, its sometimes-tarnished reputation stained even
more. The revelations would mean that every major museum
would have to inspect carefully its purchases from Brown.

Duval would never allow such a title to grace the Spoonbill list, and no other house would touch a book of this nature.

Although I have never written fiction in the espionage/ thriller category, I am convinced it is the only form in which I can cast such a bizarre story — a "truth is stranger than fiction" narrative marketed as a novel. Duval is a supreme opportunist, and I can imagine him telling me, in his most beguiling way, that my account of Gabriel Brown is my "breakthrough" title, the one that will make my name. "We could sell the book as a cross-over, a blending of biography with the best elements of detective fiction," I can hear him saying.

My heart is not in such an undertaking. I have never wanted to write such fiction, nor have I ever been drawn to non-fiction. I am damned if I do, damned if I don't — a dilemma I am quite accustomed to in my personal life, but which has never before intruded into my writing career.

HOW MUCH HAVE I forged or faked my own existence? There are the so-called harmless white lies I tell everyday: "Yes, it's a wonderful morning," and "I'm feeling on top of the world," when the truth is often "I wish I'd stayed in bed," or "I'm feeling crappy."

Stella would say I have never assumed the role of husband. I realize, sadly, that I may have playacted my part in our marriage. And Jacob tells me all the time that I am a simulacrum of a father.

At the age of eight, I was briefly a gifted — gifted because uncaught — shoplifter of toys and books. At the age of eleven, I copied a fellow classmate's Latin assignment, for which my teacher gave me a strapping. Once at grammar school I told my friend Geoff that I was not the child of Mr. and Mrs. Boyd, but rather an orphan whom they, a childless couple, had taken in. I cannot for the life of me recall precisely why I would tell such a lie, especially when the truth would have been so easily accessible to my friend. He was from a wealthy family of distinguished pedigree; perhaps, in an exceedingly childish way, I wanted to impress him. Similarly, after Oxford, I routinely told acquaintances that I had received a first when I had obtained a second.

If I am completely honest with myself, there are passages in my writings that have been lifted straight from the imaginations of Iris Murdoch, Julian Barnes, and Martin Amis. I never copied them word for word, but there are character traits and room descriptions derived from those writers, and not from my own imagination.

But borrowing bits and pieces from another writer and then reinventing them is what Shakespeare did. Imitating a great artist, affixing their name, and then selling the canvas is a different matter. It's all in the intent to deceive. If one says a canvas is by Picasso, it had better be by Picasso.

The reality is that I am a much more conventional person than I would like to be. I often wonder if one has to be really disturbed to be a great writer or a great artist. Perhaps I am angry that there are individuals who — perversely, in the instance of Brown — can turn their unhappiness into a great work of art. Am I taking my frustrations out on him not because he aspired to be an artist, but because I believe he was an authentic creator? I am envious of Brown's duplicities; no such inventiveness exists in my range. Do I resent his "greater" in comparison to my "lesser"?

I recall the Canadian writer Robertson Davies's reimagining of the incidental character: "Those roles which, being neither those of Hero nor Heroine, Confidante nor Villain, but which were nonetheless essential to bring about the Recognition or the Denouement, were called the Fifth Business in drama and opera companies organized according to the old style; the player who acted these parts was often referred to as Fifth Business."

I loathe being the Fifth Business in Gabriel Brown's glamorous existence.

CHAPTER THIRTY

A fter I return to London, I receive a call from Amelia: "Mariko, Gabriel's neighbour from across the street, has just returned from a long stay in Japan. She telephoned me last night. I think she would like to speak with you."

Amelia tells me Mariko was born in Tokyo and immigrated with her parents to Britain at the age of ten when her father, who actively disliked the militaristic turn his native land was taking, accepted the Regius Professorship of Japanese at Cambridge. When the war came, the family of three was stranded in Britain. Mariko learned first-hand the hazards of having a different colour of skin in a Western land when, at school, she was mercilessly lambasted for being born in an Axis nation.

In 1950, Mariko married a student of her father's, an Englishman. Theirs was a troubled marriage, and in 1960 she returned to Japan. She could not settle there, however, and she returned to England ten years later to resume her profession as an accountant, becoming a remarkable success in London.

MARIKO'S HOUSE, WITH its tasteful Regency exterior, resembles Brown's. Not so the inside; as soon as she opens the door, I have the impression I have travelled thousands of miles to Japan. The downstairs is one enormous room, the sections of which are separated from each other by wooden partitions about four feet high.

If I were guessing, I would say that Mariko is about fifty — but I know from Amelia that she is over eighty. She suggests we go to the sitting area, which contains a sofa and upholstered chairs.

Mariko cuts to the chase: "Under no conditions should Gabriel be subjected to such brutalization."

"That is a very strong word."

"I don't mean to offend you, but writing a biography of my friend would be like killing a butterfly with a hammer."

"I don't understand why you are taking such an adversarial position."

"Although Amelia is a dear friend, I was furious with her when she insisted I speak with you. I hoped to avoid any involvement in this matter. But because I fear the power you possess as official biographer, I am going to throw myself — and my late friend — on your mercy. And sometimes, unfortunately, honesty is the only remedy.

"Although we did not see each other often, Gabriel and I became close. He had to talk to someone, and he considered me discreet. For that reason he saw me as a safe repository for his most intimate feelings.

"On the surface, his life in retirement was uneventful. He read a great deal, took long walks on Hampstead Heath, attended the auction sales, and did a little bit of gardening. He managed to fill his days, but he was restless.

"I cannot erase from my mind the afternoon he decided to make what he called a 'full confession.' While we were drinking tea in this room, he collapsed into tears.

"'There are some evils that can never be outlived,' he told me.

"When he was a young man in Toronto, his mother's inability to deal with any aspect of her existence shook him deeply. He avoided any contact with his father because of the man's habitual drunkenness and bad temper. His sisters were in service in the suburbs, and his elder brothers had headed for British Columbia and the Yukon.

"Gabriel stayed at home for the one person he cared for deeply: his little brother Andrew. Without being fully aware of it, he saw himself as Andrew's parent.

"Once or twice, his sister Maisie had told him that she was worried something awful might befall their little brother. But he was too preoccupied with making ends meet to attend her warning.

"Then came the night that he could never erase. At eight o'clock, having just finished work, he decided to head home in order to read to Andrew before putting him to bed. When he was two streets away, Gabriel became aware of thick, billowing smoke coming from the direction of his parents' house. It quickly enveloped and blinded him, and he found it difficult to move ahead.

"When he finally reached the house, nothing more remained than a heap of charred wood. The occasional glint of smouldering ash rose into the night sky. The rank, sickly sweet smell of burning flesh filled his nostrils, never to be forgotten.

"Mrs. Ambrose, who lived four doors away, told Gabriel that his father had arrived home, blazing drunk, and had locked both the front and back doors. She heard Gabriel's mother and Andrew pleading with his father to let them out, but their cries were to no avail. Almost immediately afterwards, the house burst into flames.

"'If I had taken responsibility for Andrew,' Gabriel told me, 'he would probably still be alive. I could have saved him. I did not. I have never forgiven myself. I joined the army because I could no longer live in Canada.'"

Chapter Thirty-One
❧

I no sooner return home that evening than the phone rings. Stella, distraught and incoherent, asks me if I have had heard from Jacob.

"I think he's run away. He's not been here all day, and I just searched his room. His knapsack and most of his clothes are gone. I hoped he might be with you." She tells me that she has been trying to ring me for the past half hour.

"I suspect he's taking the piss. He'll show up here or at your place later this evening."

"He's been awfully angry at both of us."

I suggest we wait until the morning to inform the police, and then retreat to the den. All I can do is stare senselessly at Brown's library — a place in which my son has also been taking refuge recently.

When I was Jacob's age, I too had tried to run away from home. I spent a day on British Rail, intending to make my way to Southampton to stow aboard a liner heading for Canada. Though I only had a backpack and ten quid, I thought I had a reasonable chance of success; I was well read in Robert Louis Stevenson and Richard Henry Dana and was sure my survival skills would assist me in returning to the country of my birth. But my stomach was my undoing. I lasted a total of five hours — my mother never even found out that I had skipped school.

That was also the year I saw Monet's *Water Lilies* at Musée de l'Orangerie. Once, I told Jacob how moved I was by the installation: "It is Giverny in the heart of Paris. Eight stunning compositions divided into twenty-two panels in two rooms. It doesn't get much better."

In a flash, the penny drops. I immediately telephone Stella. "Everything's going to be alright. I'm certain I know what he's up to. I'm leaving shortly to retrieve him — I'll phone you tomorrow afternoon with an update."

I AM TOO late to take the Eurostar this evening. Instead, I make the crossing the next morning to arrive in Paris by ten o'clock. Then I take a taxi to the Orangerie.

I come upon Jacob seated before *Morning with Weeping Willows*. I can see from the expression on his face that he has reached an understanding similar to Proust's:

> Here and there, on the surface, like a strawberry, a waterlily reddens: a scarlet heart and white edges. Further on, the flowers grow in numbers and are paler, rougher, grainier, more crinkled and haphazardly dispersed in mounds so graciously that you would think they are floating astray, like the melancholic farewells after a festivity, with bubbly roses forming unraveled garlands.

"YOU'RE EXACTLY ON time," Jacobs snickers. Then, with a heaping dollop of condescension, he says, "You're maturing, Dad. You're becoming a grown-up."

I am beginning to take such remarks in stride. "I have a few fatherly things to say to you on such matters, but I have to phone your mother first."

WHEN I RETURN to the *Water Lilies*, Jacob suggests we walk around the two enormous galleries at the Orangerie.

"I came here because working on Mr. Brown's biography messed you up. I got worried."

"About me?"

"Yes. Of course. I could see the book was draining you. You weren't my dad. You were Guy."

"I became over-preoccupied."

"I wanted you to look at something else. Freshen your eyes up. You had to see pure works of art," he remarks. "I was here yesterday afternoon and evening too. I looked at all the other pictures here, especially the Kees van Dongen portrait of Paul Guillaume."

The portrait of Guillaume is of a self-absorbed dandy, perhaps a bit like Prufrock. I recall that Guillaume was a youngster working in a garage when he came upon some African sculptures in a cargo box. The startling discovery hooked him and led to his opening a small gallery in 1914. Until his death in 1934, he exhibited the new modern masters: Picasso, Picabia, de Chirico, and Modigliani. Like Gabriel Brown, he was a charming and persuasive salesman.

When I finish inspecting the canvases, Jacob tells me his thoughts, aided by ample use of the Internet. "Gabriel Brown saw himself as the English Paul Guillaume. But if you look at the Guillaume, you see someone who was pleased with himself. I don't think Mr. Brown had much joy in himself. If Ralph and I were to re-do our Lego portrait, the tragic would have to inhabit that countenance."

I like that last little bit of art history jargon. "I think that your assumptions are correct." Then, I somewhat hesitantly do my best to remind Jacob that, precocious as he may be, he is still a child who must obey parental rules. He nods at appropriate points as I dispense my pearls of wisdom. I think there is a decent chance he might heed what I say.

We also reach a firm agreement: in a year or two, we will travel to Canada, so he can inspect the country where I was born.

"I also want to visit Toronto so that I can understand Mr. Brown more," he informs me.

Perhaps it is Jacob who has the instincts of a life writer?

Chapter Thirty-Two

I would not mind relinquishing the Brown project. I am capable of breaking the bad news to Duval. I am resigned to returning to my former humdrum existence. However, I do not wish to disappoint Amelia, and will do anything in my power to postpone the inevitable conversation with her. She will be devastated.

As I try to figure out my next step, she phones: "I have another person for you to interview. Her name is Alice Gagnon."

"The name does not ring a bell."

"She's a Canadian collector who met Gabriel long after he closed the gallery, and who became good friends with him. They always met when she came to London for the Sotheby's and Christie's sales. I was going to mention her to you when you were on your way to Canada, but I knew she was travelling in Vietnam and Cambodia. Then her name slipped my mind. I have met her twice. She is a wonderful person. You should probably see her."

ALICE GAGNON ANSWERS my email request for an interview a few hours after I send it. She would be happy to see me, and suggests we meet in her suite at the Savoy.

Googling Gagnon produces a number of results, but surprisingly no photographs. The various links all contain the same information: she is well over eighty, has been retired for almost twenty years, and her hobbies are collecting and travelling. She began her working life as a lowly clerk in a large firm that manufactures boxes, and rose slowly but steadily within that company. Her genius is in the careful management of assets, in the delegation of power to others, and in employing cutting-edge designers. Resolutely, she held out against the lure of China, and has become something of a national heroine by sticking to a Made in Canada policy. In no way is she a typical captain of industry; in fact, she has gone proudly against the grain.

I HAVE NEVER been inside the Savoy, though I have walked by its recessed entranceway off the Strand many times. From that distance it looks unfriendly and bleak; not so when I finally enter its elegant art deco portals and take the elevator up to the fifteenth floor.

The woman who answers the door resembles a Parisian sparrow. Not quite five feet tall, she holds herself like an aristocrat. Her pale lavender dress is quietly expensive; her matching shoes could be called dainty. Bright red rouge and crimson lipstick are her only adornments. Her thin black hair is not coloured and contains a few flecks of white. Her dark brown eyes are large, her other features small. She is remarkably attractive for her age; she reminds me of Celia Johnson as Laura Jesson in *Brief Encounter*. Her quiet loveliness gives her a sedate appearance, but steely strength of character is visible in her eyes. That must be the key to her success: she is a powerful person who never resorts to bad temper or threats.

After shaking my hand, she invites me to sit on the sofa in her good-sized sitting room. The room is elegant in a subdued way: soft colours for the stuffed furniture, a Chippendale-inspired bureau and desk worthy of my father's best work, and a medium-sized silk Oriental rug sitting on top of the cream-coloured wall-to-wall carpeting.

The lady takes the chair opposite me and says, "Amelia thinks the world of you. She has told me wonderful things."

"Miss Bryant is far too generous. It is her only fault."

She smiles. "That is a nice way of complimenting a friend. I see we are going to be such."

For the next twenty minutes, we talk about London and Toronto. I tell her about my background and my only visit to Canada. A keen listener, she stops me once or twice briefly to ask a question.

When the formalities are over, she turns to business. "I came to art late in the day. To be honest, I had previously gone, sort of duty-bound, to a number of exhibitions at the Art Gallery of Ontario in Toronto and the National Gallery in Ottawa. I looked, but I never really saw. Until I met Gabriel."

She pours our tea. "Collecting can be a nerve-racking undertaking even if you have a great deal of money. Many of the dealers want you to establish your bona fides with them by acquiring the leavings no one else wants — a third-rate Utrillo, a hastily painted Signac. I had no patience for those; after I retired, I began travelling to England for the spring and autumn auction sales of Old Masters. I would always arrive in London well in advance of a sale, attend the previews, do my research at the British Library, and then decide on one or two pictures to bid on. I was attracted to the Post-Impressionists.

"On my fourth or fifth foray to London, I made a pilgrimage during the previews to admire a small Seurat I had decided to pursue. 'It approaches perfection, does it not?' said a voice behind me. I turned around to behold a tall, elderly man speaking to me in what I knew was an Ontarian accent.

"That was the start of our relationship. We always met when I came to London and talked pictures together for hours on end. He often told me, 'It is a sin to make one's living selling beautiful objects.'"

Miss Gagnon then tells me about the splendid Matisses, Signacs, and Gauguins she acquired with her friend's help. When I take my leave, she insists we get together the next time she is in London.

CHAPTER THIRTY-THREE

The next day, I am startled when Alice Gagnon phones me.

"There is an aspect of my relationship with Gabriel that we did not discuss yesterday. Can I ask that we meet at your home rather than here? I'll explain my unusual request when we see each other."

Gagnon's hired car arrives at exactly three o'clock. She is ruffled, and her calm air of assurance has vanished. "Is the large bedroom upstairs vacant?"

"Yes. I never go there."

"Would you mind if we visit it?"

We walk up. I open the door for her and follow her in. "It was empty when I arrived," I inform her. My voice echoes.

"I have only been here once before. The floor space was, as now, completely empty. There were, however, six Van Goghs on the wall."

"They seem to have disappeared. I have never heard tell of them," I lie. Diego told me Brown had offered five of them to

Sir George Armstrong years before; perhaps they were the last of his forgeries.

"I would be surprised if you knew anything about them. All six are in my collection."

My stomach churns. I do not know if I can conceal my dismay. Had Brown been scouring the auction houses in pursuit of prey? Had he hoodwinked Miss Gagnon?

Oblivious to my discomfort, she walks around the room and points out the slightly lighter patches on the beige walls. "If you look carefully, you can see where each of the canvases was. I have never forgotten the thrill I received when Gabriel took me here. I was under the impression that he only collected modern master prints, until that afternoon, when he allowed me to see the hidden masterpieces. Six paintings from Van Gogh's Arles period. Five landscapes and one self-portrait.

"As we carefully inspected each in turn, he told me the full story of their discovery. He was vacationing in a small town near Arles, where he quizzed people about pictures that had been in their families for two or three generations. One day, a young fellow approached him and told him that his recently deceased grandmother owned some wonderful copies of Van Goghs made shortly after the artist's death, and would Mr. Brown like to see them?

"Two days later, he visited the old woman's house. The paintings had been placed one on top of another in the sitting room. Gabriel looked at each in turn and then started to question the grandson. The young man said that his grandmother had been assured the paintings were authentic when she was a girl. After she inherited them, she showed them to some dealers, who informed her they were copies.

"Gabriel was blunt with him: they might be originals. The young man was not interested in that possibility, so Gabriel offered him a million pounds for the lot.

"When the pictures arrived in London, he kept them in this room and allowed no one to see them. Over the years, he conducted research that led him to be certain that the grand-mother had, as a girl, been told the truth. They were authentic."

I squirm, but Alice is still oblivious. "That afternoon Gabriel offered me all six paintings. The price was high, but not high for Van Gogh. Forty million dollars."

I almost groan.

"What was strange about the purchase price was that not a cent was to go to Gabriel. Instead, the money was to be dispersed to ten charities of my choice — although he suggested I select organizations that actively helped the poor. I pressed him about the financial arrangements, but he bluntly told me that he did not need the money. He said, 'I would like the paintings to go to someone who will enjoy them. At the same time, I would like their purchase price to benefit the unfortunate. I also know that you will be sure the paintings will ultimately make their way into a major museum in Canada.' I immediately agreed to his terms, and we walked downstairs and drank our tea."

AS SHE TAKES her leave, Alice informs me of her plan to "introduce" her six Van Goghs to Toronto the following month. She has hired a suitable exhibition space in the central part of the city, and she would like me to see the show.

"If you attend, you will perhaps know Gabriel even better than you do now."

I tell her that I will be there.

THE DAY AFTER Alice's visit, I wander the room that once held the Van Goghs. I close my eyes, breathe deeply, and catch the slightest scene of turpentine. Brown had not completely covered his tracks.

Every time I think I understand Brown's deviousness, a new side of his duplicitous nature asserts itself. What complicated game, I ask myself, had he been playing? Had he used Gagnon's money to assuage his conscience? Had he attempted to find permanent homes for his finest fakes, to prove once again that there was no expert he could not fool? Had there been even a shred of altruism in what he had done? Should I make the truth known to her?

CHAPTER THIRTY-FOUR

～

En route to Toronto, I fly to Boston to spend a day at Harvard's Fogg Museum. Gagnon had told me that her Van Gogh was a variant of his *Self-Portrait as a Japanese Bonze*, and I wish to see that celebrated impersonation.

Van Gogh is a difficult artist to study if one relies on reproductions. Even the finest ones do not allow the viewer to see how the thickly applied paint creates shadows that move according to how much light is available. Light and shadow change as the viewer moves left to right. The canvas alters dramatically based on the viewer's proximity; a Van Gogh canvas always looks very differently from two feet than it does from five. The dense, swirling lines of a Van Gogh mean that his pictures are never still. They are always in the process of becoming.

The Harvard self-portrait is one of the consummate Van Gogh images. The face is soft, the eyes almond-shaped, the nose aquiline, the moustache and beard neatly trimmed. The blue background is complemented by the zigzagging dark blue bordering the sitter's waistcoat and vest. The picture, dedicated to Gauguin, courts the other man's approval; it shows Van Gogh on his best behaviour, for once not confronting the viewer sternly. The serenity is seductive: this is the portrait of the artist as a refined aesthete.

VINCENT VAN GOGH was not a likeable person. He was desperately needy and excessively self-centred. His brother Theo, who ministered to him as best he could, forsook his own identity, allowing himself to be cannibalized by Vincent the artist.

In addition, Van Gogh was messy, disheveled, smelly, frequently rude, and often inebriated. He was a frequent visitor to bordellos, where he often treated the women poorly. When need arose, he could be mendacious. He exaggerated the living conditions at the Yellow House, an excuse for living quarters that he had deluded himself into thinking was a long-lost Eden, in order to convince Gauguin to stay with him.

Desperate for the other man's companionship, he told Gauguin: "I have just rented a four-room house here in Arles. And that it would seem that if I could find another painter inclined to work in the South, and who, like myself, would be sufficiently absorbed in his work to be able to resign himself to living like a monk who goes to the brothel once a fortnight, it might be a good job."

Gauguin, a much more crafty and fastidious person than his Dutch friend, was disappointed in his new residence. The stage was set for their constant arguments, which led to Van Gogh amputating part of his own left ear.

The man endured incredible anguish. He loved the colours and textures of nature, but he hated himself. His mind was filled with chaotic, racing thoughts that he harnessed to create rhapsodic canvases that precisely capture the beauties of the natural world.

Like Picasso, he was both creator and destroyer. I often wonder if these two men are placed so high in our contemporary pantheon of true artistic genius because they were so badly behaved. In their existences we find little evidence of heroic greatness. But that may be the point. In our narcissistic world, they are examples of deeply troubled men who nevertheless made great art. They provide us with a level playing field: they are just as vulnerable — or awful — as we are.

Van Gogh is the favourite of many because he gave everything in the service of his profession. He insisted that beauty exists even when one is held captive by despair and self-loathing. Though he took his own life, he embodies the idea that beauty can triumph over misery. Visitors to museums want to behold the markings this remarkable being made on canvas. They want to bear witness to his life, to see the remaining evidence of his existence.

To my way of thinking, there is something inherently sacrilegious in faking a Van Gogh. Brown's hubris, I remind myself, is more limitless than I had imagined.

～

THE FLIGHT FROM Boston to Toronto is just over an hour. This time, at her insistence, I am staying with Alice Gagnon. "You're only here for three days, and I want to spend as much time with you as possible."

She is in a state of unbridled excitement. The exhibition opened the day before, and has been subject to a barrage of media coverage. She spent two long days at the entranceway greeting the steady stream of visitors. "I didn't plan to stay so long, but many of the visitors seem to expect this. Many of them want to chat after the experience."

Gagnon rents a large sunny flat on the seventeenth floor of Hazelton Lanes in Yorkville. The sitting room looks as if it was decorated by Vuillard. The thick, luxuriant wallpapers are brightly coloured and flecked with gold and silver, and the sofas are overstuffed and covered with velvet. My feet sink into the Oriental rugs, most of them ablaze with vivid reds, oranges, and yellows.

The interior decoration has been carefully selected to accompany the canvases on the wall: two Vuillards, a Dufy, a Pissarro, and four small Matisses. I can easily imagine myself inside some grand flat in Nice overlooking the Promenade des Anglais, the ghosts of Henry James and Edith Wharton comfortably at home in the setting.

There are six large empty spaces on the wall. Though bright, the room seems in mourning, incomplete without the canvases now on display elsewhere in the city.

"This place is not itself without the Vincents," Alice confides in a matter-of-fact voice. "I am happy to share them with others, but I long to have them back. I was not surprised to discover how forlorn that room in Gabriel's house looked without them."

I ARRIVE AT the exhibition at eleven and join a long queue waiting to get inside, having asked Gagnon to go ahead without me: "I don't want to be there when it opens. I will enjoy mingling with the others visiting the show."

A handful of children accompany their parents. I am

surprised that these youngsters are so well-mannered. Every-one waits patiently and good-naturedly, and become quiet when they enter the antechamber. Gagnon is there, nodding sagely at her guests. She plays the part of the gracious hostess to perfection.

I realize now how vulnerable she is. These paintings are her children, and she wishes for them to be accepted as her offspring. She wants them to be loved.

I must keep my findings to myself. Even if I am able to pin Brown down as a cheat, it would be a pyrrhic victory at best. If I announce that I have been correct all along, I would be accessing the most selfish, self-aggrandizing part of myself. If I play the role of spoiler, Gabriel Brown will have bested me.

CHAPTER THIRTY-FIVE

Inscribed on the walls of the antechamber is a brief statement:

These six Van Goghs were once owned by the late Mr. Gabriel
Brown, the renowned English art dealer, who sold them
in 1998 to Alice Gagnon. Her fond hope is that the six
paintings will, after her death, become part of the collection
of a major gallery in Canada.

The clear implication is that the lady wishes to donate the
six oils to a major public collection, provided they keep all
six together.

The paintings are on display in the large gallery, each with
a bevy of accessory information surrounding it — excerpts
from Van Gogh's letters describing work on this particular
subject, as well as full-size reproductions of similar paintings
in the artist's canon.

Printed on the wall at the entrance to the room is an introduction by Brown himself. Next to each painting, as well, is a brief description written by him.

A SHORT INTRODUCTION: VAN GOGH IN ARLES

I came upon these six canvases while visiting Arles in 1980, almost one hundred years after they were painted in 1888–9. They were in my possession until they entered the collection of Alice Gagnon in 1998. None of these oils is a typical blockbuster Arles image. In each of the pictures here the tonalities tend to be sombre, almost melancholic. They do not display, for example, the sensational colours found in Van Gogh's depiction of his bedroom or in *The Night Café*. Instead, the viewer sees an undisguised Vincent, a man cast adrift, the great artist imprisoned in self-loathing. Yet, in each of the landscapes, the artist rises above his sense of fragility to show us the majesty of the physical world. Despite suffering, they insist, triumph is possible.

Perhaps this is why we love Van Gogh: in the face of our own shortcomings and failures, he reminds us that there is a higher reality to which we are connected. When we look at his paintings, we enter that sphere of existence. We are redeemed.

I walk around the gallery slowly, studying each picture carefully and taking note of Brown's observations.

Field with Haystacks: The green-blue field and the green haystacks are juxtaposed in an almost wave-like formation that reminds one of Hokusai. The wheat sheaves are like a huge boat trying to anchor itself, with some difficulty, in the green sea surrounding it. The pale blue sky relieves some of the tension between the haystacks and the field. The sheaves must fight to survive, and they do so with complete self-assurance. Resilience is the cornerstone of any successful attempt to stay fully alive. The painting proclaims this truth, although Vincent never possessed such suppleness.

Vines: The quirky blue-coloured vines, green shrubbery, and brown earth are depicted and then separated from each other, a technique characteristic of the cloisonnist style, whereby bold, flat forms are separated from each other by dark contours. Here the effect is deliberately claustrophobic and confusing. Van Gogh is reminding his viewer that there are many parts of the natural world that will evade us even if we pay close attention to them.

View of Irises with Arles in the Background: Perhaps the most conventional of the images on display. From a distance this is a somewhat ordinary, lacklustre canvas. Move closer, though, and the intensity of the quick, darting brushstrokes of the irises and the field is overpowering. In Van Gogh's world, there is always more than the eye can absorb.

Sheaves of Wheat: Another splendid example of Van Gogh's work in the cloisonnist style. Here, the yellows and oranges of the sheaves are demarcated by blue and gold. Each of the sheaves is an experiment in form: they may be still, but each seems to have its own personality. The light and dark greens in the background and the beige in the foreground both relieve and highlight the sheaves occupying most of the picture area. This oil, slightly larger than the similar image in the collection of the Dallas Art Museum, shows Van Gogh in his most rhapsodic, exuberant mode.

Les Alyscamps: Thousands of randomly assorted sarcophagi lie strewn in the middle of Arles. In other paintings of the same subject, Van Gogh shows strollers visiting the ruins, but here no human presence intervenes. The viewer looks through tree trunks at what is a poignant *memento mori*. The dark blue of the trees contrasts with the earthy colours of the path through the ancient, green and yellow coffin-like structures. Van Gogh confronts the fact of death squarely here: the earth is a place of incredible beauty, but the artist will not always be a part of it. Death erases us.

I have to pause before examining the self-portrait, a canvas I am sure Brown never offered for sale. I cannot detect, in any of the five landscapes, a single slip into inauthenticity; the forger has done his work in consummate fashion. The colours and the brushstrokes look like Van Gogh's. Each canvas exudes passion.

I am left with unsettling questions: Did Brown choose the Arles period because Van Gogh was poised between elation and despair during that brief portion of his life? Had Brown seen his own existence oscillating between similar extremes? Was he able to maintain a calm exterior while his inner world was in danger of collapse? Is this why he identified so strongly with Van Gogh? Did he paint these pictures because they allowed him to confront his own despair-filled existence and, even fleetingly, obtain mastery over it?

As I delight in the perfection of each painting, I feel the presence of the deeply damaged person who created it. I see Brown imprinting his own suffering onto each of these canvases. I imagine him reliving the loss of his brother as he applies the paint thickly to each. I behold him gaining relief from his anguish as he works feverishly. Gabriel Brown becomes Van Gogh.

His words about the self-portrait are spare, even terse:

Self Portrait. This version of Van Gogh as a bonze is significantly larger than the one at the Fogg Museum at Harvard University. This is a picture about renunciation and forgiveness. The sitter, in allowing himself to move outside the confines of his small world, is in this moment able to bestow some compassion upon himself.

Much more could be said. The background in this version is a warm pink, with flecks of red scattered throughout. The subject faces the viewer much more directly than his Harvard counterpart. The jacket and shirt are in lighter shades of brown. The skeletal cheekbones, the clipped beard, the moustache, and the balding top of the head are virtually identical.

The eyes, however, are vastly different. They are defiant. These are the eyes I first encountered in the photograph in the City of Toronto Archives. They do not possess the tranquil, resigned look of the Harvard portrait. Their look is one of cunning, triumph, and endurance. This is the face of a man who refuses to be defeated. He is a fighter, a man who will do battle with the contrary forces threatening him. He would never have cut off a portion of his own ear.

It does not matter what name is affixed to this canvas: it is a masterpiece. Who am I to quarrel with such genius? Before such a miracle of invention, I surrender.

CHAPTER THIRTY-SIX

🍂

I contemplate my interview with Amelia.

Though I am not partial to much of Conrad's *Heart of Darkness*, I find the concluding section of the novella — Marlow's encounter with Kurtz's fiancée, the Intended — riveting. Marlow has come to loathe Kurtz and all that he represents. In Kurtz he sees a clear reflection of his own propensity to commit evil. There but for the grace of God go I, he tells himself. When he goes to his meeting with Kurtz's beloved, Marlow is a depressed but newly self-educated person. In his heart of hearts, Marlow knows that he should tell this woman the truth: her beloved was a scoundrel who ran amok in the jungle. However, the woman has a completely idealized remembrance of the man she was supposed to marry, and if Marlow tells her the truth he knows she will be destroyed. The pain that the Intended will suffer holds Marlow back, and he allows Kurtz's posthumous reputation to remain intact. He views himself as a coward, albeit one who acts this way to save another person.

I am trapped in the Marlow scenario. I do not wish to tell Amelia the truth; I would prefer to inform her that I have discovered virtually nothing about Gabriel, and let the matter die a natural death. No book. End of story. Such an ending would be the fairy tale version of Brown's life.

Fragments of *Heart of Darkness* invade my consciousness:

> She came forward, all in black, with a pale head, floating towards me in the dusk. She was in mourning ... She took both my hands in hers and murmured, "I had heard you were coming." I noticed she was not very young — I mean not girlish. She had a mature capacity for fidelity, for belief, for suffering. The room seemed to have grown darker, as if all the sad light of the cloudy evening had taken refuge on her forehead. This fair hair, this pale visage, this pure brow, seemed surrounded by an ashy halo from which the dark eyes looked out at me. Their glance was guileless, profound, confident, and trustful. She carried her sorrowful head as though she were proud of that sorrow, as though she would say, "I — I alone know how to mourn for him as he deserves."

This morning Amelia is dressed in a chic pale blue silk dress, in contrast to her usual dowdy yellow cardigan and black trousers. She carries herself differently, as if a tremendous burden has been lifted from her psyche. As usual, she kisses me at the door.

We make small talk for about ten minutes. Then, I know, I need to discuss Gabriel Brown. "He was a remarkable man," I say unsteadily. The fixity of her gaze seems to demand more words from my lips, so I go on: "It is impossible not to —"

Amelia interrupts me. "It is impossible not to be aghast at some of the horrible deeds he committed," she states calmly.

I am stunned.

She looks me full in the face before continuing. "I commissioned Spoonbill to find a biographer because I entertained some grave doubts about Gabriel. The twenty-fifth-anniversary catalogue troubled me: all of the sitters look a bit like Gabriel. No one else ever made the connection, and I thought there was something wrong with me. But when you arrived back from your first trip to Canada, I knew something was not right. You had an edge to your voice; your demeanour told me you had discovered some unpleasant truths about my old boss." She smiles. "I do regret putting you in a position to act as a detective. Aren't all biographers really private investigators, though? People who snoop around in the dirty linen of others? I have become far too fond of you to allow you to continue any longer in that dubious profession."

I am relieved. I can tell Amelia the full story.

I tell her about my discoveries in Toronto. She is on the verge of tears as I recount the struggles of young John Martin. She cries softly when I tell her about the death of his brother. She is intrigued by my adventures in Spain.

"I think Diego is a wise man," she says.

Then I tell her of my last stay in Toronto. "I no longer dislike Brown. In his own way, he was a great artist. Perhaps forgery was the only way he could get in touch with his real self."

Like me, Amelia is torn. "Despite misgivings, I still retain the highest esteem for Gabriel. I love him as the brother I never had. Such an affection cannot be eradicated."

CHAPTER THIRTY-SEVEN
❧

The Spoonbill offices have been transformed since my last visit six months ago. I am certain the funds for this remarkable metamorphosis — new blinds, carpeting, desks, an iMac on every desk, a huge state-of-the-art Xerox machine — have flowed from Miss Bryant's beneficence.

As for me, I am up in the air. I'm afraid I'll soon be on the dole.

Some things never change. Duval is dressed exactly as he was on the day he commissioned the biography, and gets straight to the point: "Miss Bryant has pulled the plug on the biography. She told me there is insufficient material for such a book, and thinks it might be best to forego any kind of volume memorializing Mr. Brown."

He takes a significant pause.

"You are not being turned out into the cruel world, Guy. Miss Bryant is your benefactor. She has determined that you are to become the new owner of Gabriel Brown's house. You are also to be paid the full sum of the advance. As you recall, you have already received but a third of that munificent amount. In the lottery of life, you have been transformed into a winner."

"I am deeply grateful to the lady — and to you — for putting me on to what was, although short-lived, a remarkable scheme."

"Quite so. I wish that Mr. Carstairs could pop in to say a word or two. He would second my congratulations in the warmest possible terms. Unfortunately, he has been unwell and is resting in his villa in the south of France."

CHAPTER THIRTY-EIGHT

I am blunt with Amelia in that she has been far too generous in giving me Brown's house.

She is equally forthright: "It's yours. You must do with it what you see fit."

As for the remainder of the large advance, I tell her that I have resolved to spend the next year writing a new novel. "Perhaps I can go in a new direction? I'm not making plans beyond that."

The novel I am currently writing is not going well. It concerns a celebrated hematologist whose findings, which revolutionize all previous conceptions about how blood circulates, have had incalculable benefits, particularly to newborns. He is at the peak of his career, and is on the verge of being awarded the Nobel Prize.

The hematologist's apprentice stumbles upon the truth. The man's entire career is built on a falsehood: he had applied to medical school with false credentials.

The younger man must decide whether to expose his master. Though he is fully aware of the fundamental contribution his mentor's research has made to the physical well-being of millions, he tells himself that the truth must out. He also realizes that he is deeply envious of the older man.

I am going to abandon this book.

The "real" Gabriel Brown's life history is the only story I feel drawn to tell. He will be my inspiration; perhaps I can transform my biography into a novel. If I make up large parts of his existence, I'm sure he will understand completely.